A Speech Pathologist
Talks to
Parents and Teachers

Courtesy The Ohio State University.

A speech clinician shows a mother how to encourage speech through the use of the grocery-store situation. The child names the items he wants; the mother repeats them so the child will hear the correct auditory pattern.

A SPEECH PATHOLOGIST TALKS TO PARENTS AND TEACHERS

For Teacher and Parent Education
in Speech and Related Problems

by

RUTH BECKEY IRWIN, Ph.D.

Professor of Speech
The Ohio State University

STANWIX HOUSE, INC.   Pittsburgh

Copyright 1962 by Stanwix House, Inc.
Printed in the United States of America.

All rights reserved. No part of this book may be used or reproduced in any manner whatsoever without written permission except in the case of brief quotations embodied in critical articles and reviews. For information address Stanwix House, Inc., 3020 Chartiers Avenue, Pittsburgh, Pennsylvania 15204.

Published simultaneously in Canada by
J. M. Dent & Sons (Canada) Ltd.
Toronto, Ontario

First Printing—June 1962
Second Printing—April 1966
Third Printing—January 1968

Library of Congress Catalog Card Number:
62–14634

Preface

Children With Crippled Speech

"What can I do with my little girl? She is five years old and doesn't talk plainly yet. I took her to the doctor and he doesn't give me any satisfaction. I took her to the public schools and they say that she'll just have to outgrow it. I don't want my little girl to be handicapped so early in life. What am I to do? Who is able to help me?"

That is the universal plea among mothers of children with crippled speech. Children may have defective speech as a result of disease, injury, poor environment, or a combination of factors. Whatever the reason, someone in the community should be able to help a mother with such a problem. Society does a tragic injustice to the child with a speech handicap or related problem when no attempt is made to help him.

In one school, a girl with a severe articulatory defect was allowed to proceed in school until she was a senior in high school. Finally, the girl wandered into the university speech clinic. She spoke so inarticulately that the clinician could not understand her—she had to write her message! Yet, one of her teachers in the high school did not even know that she had a speech defect! She had never talked in class! This girl's one desire was to talk like other girls her age, and she succeeded. However, how unfortunate it was for this girl that she lived such an abnormal life for so many years.

In another school, a young boy of twelve was misunderstood and ill-treated because he stuttered. Teachers would not allow him to talk, even though he occasionally volunteered. He received low marks since he did not talk in school; yet his intelligence was found to be above normal. Such negligence on the part of society produces many maladjusted personalities and may lead to delinquencies.

Teachers may do much to help with the situation. In the first place, they may improve their own speech. The teacher needs to be acquainted with normal production of all speech sounds; she needs to be able to compare her own speech with that of others; and she needs to be able to hear the difference between the normal and defective sounds.

The teacher needs to be a good example. For instance, in one teacher education institution, a teacher of the primary grades not only lisped but talked as though her mouth were full of mush. As a result, many of the children in the room also used poor speech.

At one time, a speech clinician was making a survey of the speech deviations in a certain school system. Upon entering the first-grade room, she asked the teacher, "Do any of your children have speech problems?"

"Oh, no, the children in this room speak perfectly," she answered with a dull *s* sound that was almost a *th* .

However, the speech clinician was granted permission to examine the children. She was not surprised to find that many of the children had copied their teacher's dull *s* sound.

Consequently, the teacher's own speech is very important. This can also be said about the mother's or father's speech. The child usually learns what he hears as far as speech is concerned. The small child with a German grandmother may speak some of the sounds correctly but the *w* always appears as *v*. Speech is learned! It is not inherited!

In the second place, the teacher should take a course in speech-correction methods, so that she will be able to diagnose the severe speech disorders and be able to recommend to the parents what to do. Furthermore, she should be able to correct the minor disorders herself. How unfortunate is the kindergarten teacher who does not know enough about the simple speech disorders among children to help them at all.

In the third place, the teacher needs to know how to stimulate speech improvement in the regular classroom through the use of choral speaking activities, creative dramatics, sharing time, discussion periods, and oral reports. Many speech activities may be coordinated with other school work, so that the busy teacher will not have an added burden. Special references for the teacher are included in the Appendix of this book.

What can the parents do? The parents and teachers need to work together in order to be most effective in helping the speech-handicapped child. The community with a speech clinician is fortunate. The parent can look to the clinician for guidance. Both parents and teachers will work with the clinician for best results.

In communities where there is not a speech clinician, the parents may initiate some interest by talking with the local superintendent about their needs. Information concerning a state program and financial assistance to local programs may be obtained by writing to the State Department of Education.

In addition to promoting services for the speech-handicapped child and cooperating with the teachers and clinician (if there is one), the parent will improve his own speech so as to furnish an adequate speech model for the child.

Until quite recently, mothers and fathers accepted their speech-handicapped children as a "cross which they must bear." They did not know that something could be done to help the hard-of-hearing, cerebral-palsied, stuttering, inarticulate, or speechless child to talk acceptably.

Even now, many persons crippled in speech do not know that speech freedom is available for them. Consequently, every effort should be made to encourage state departments of education, and others, to extend this much-needed service to the children with the "crippled tongues."

Almost all of the states of the union now have some legislative provision for extending services to the speech-handicapped children. Do you know what services your state provides?

Ruth Beckey Irwin

Introduction

How to Use This Book

The purpose for compiling this material in book form is to make available more readily the information for use by parents, teachers, and speech clinicians. One of the principal reasons for assembling the various topics in this book is the anticipation of its possible use by parent-teacher groups which desire to use the book as a "text" for study sessions. Another reason for presenting the material in its present form is for its use by public-school speech and hearing clinicians who want to have source material for conducting in-service training courses for teachers or parents. For this reason, problems and references are included at the end of each chapter.

Because this book is intended for parents and teachers as well as the speech clinician, the speech sounds cited herein are printed in pronunciation symbols rather than phonetic symbols. For example, when the text refers to the "ch" sound as in *chair* or *watch*, the pronunciation symbol *ch* will be given rather than the phonetic symbol tʃ. These pronunciation symbols are the same as would be found in any dictionary.

Major Objectives

In planning meetings, what should be the major objectives? These are a few of the aims toward which any parent who is interested in helping his handicapped child should work: (1) To face problems realistically, (2) To recognize and improve his own speech problems, (3) To understand the nature and causes of speech problems, (4) To learn about related problems, such as hearing loss and reading disability, and (5) To study children's adjustment problems and relationship to language development.

Organization of Meetings

At least six meetings should be arranged. Probably, not more than two-week intervals between meetings should be allowed. Preferably, the parents' group should meet each week. In college and university clinics, the parents often attend a class at the same time their children receive speech therapy. Some public-school groups prefer to hold a few meetings in the evening so that the fathers can attend also. Suggested programs for parents and teachers are included in the Appendix.

For the first meeting, some speaker, such as a psychologist, physician, or a professional speech person from the nearest university, may be invited to talk. For the most part, the speech clinician and the parents can rely upon their own resources. Moreover, learning experiences on the part of the parents or teachers may be much more productive if they themselves take part frequently in the discussions. Parents and teachers certainly have a wealth of experiences with which to illustrate much of the material which is found in books regarding children. Group discussion will allow the participants an opportunity to ask questions about reading materials as well as to discover that others have very similar problems.

Discussion of Behavior Problems

Invariably, parents will ask questions during discussion periods about behavior or conduct. Although little scientific evidence supports the close relationship of behavior problems to speech and/or hearing deviations, controlled observations indicate that children with communicative disorders usually have more than their share of poor habits or personality irregularities.

Consequently, it seems desirable to include a large segment on behavior problems in any well-rounded parent-education program. Some clinicians feel that the improvement of personality will indirectly have important bearing on the reduction or removal of speech deviations. The changed attitude or method of handling children by the parents can be more important than any direct therapy, especially for the young child.

If the clinician does not have a strong background in clinical

Introduction

or child psychology, a child psychologist probably should be asked to speak to the group as well as to be ready to lead the discussion. For the clinician who is qualified to lead a discussion on behavior problems, the following outline may serve as a guide to the study of various conduct problems:

1. Choose a general topic on conduct or behavior based on needs and interests of parents.

2. Prepare a set of questions and answers on the topic based on experience, observation, and research. Answers should include references. Members of the group may be encouraged to write the answers to two or three of the questions ahead of time in order to add some motivation to the discussion.

3. Give some kind of assignment:
   A. Record one day's experience.
   B. Keep a record of your child's behavior for one week.

Discussion Leads to Insight

An indirect method of discussion of problems is often used by clinicians to aid parents to gain insight into the factors which may be affecting their child's speech. The following excerpt from a report of a clinician describes a procedure with one parents' group:

"We discussed the parents' personal adjustment and its effect on the child. We attempted to show the group how important it is for the parent to be well-adjusted to his economic and social status so there will be no ill effect on the children. The members of the group were asked how the lack of adjustment might be exhibited in actions toward the child. This led us back to such words as *resentment* and *affection*. These were discussed in terms of what they mean and how these feelings are arrived at in their children. With appropriate introductions, it was suggested that they write down just what they do to show their love for their children. This was done and the general answers were talked about during the next meeting. One response was, 'When *T* comes to ask me if I love him, I assure him that I do!' As we talked about this statement, we found ourselves wondering why the child should have to ask if he is loved. This led us to another step—that of writing down those things we do which might give the child the impression that he is not wanted or not loved."

The following questions represent some of the inquiries of the parents in one discussion group:

1. "My boy has been working on the sound *p* which he can say all right in some cases. But he still says his name, Phillip, as 'Fulp'."

2. "I'm scared to death of the day that Tommy finds out that he's different. What can I do?"

3. "My children learned to dress very rapidly, but once they learned they expected me to do it for them."

4. "My grandson can tie his shoes, but he waits for me to do it."

5. "What skills can I expect my child to have for his age, especially in speech?"

6. "What speech standards should I hold for my child?"

7. "My child always acts up and gets wild when company comes."

8. "I have a friend who always answers her child's questions, even if the child is talking with someone else. That seems unfair, and impolite to the child."

These and many other questions will be raised as the clinician and parents talk together concerning the various aspects of the speech problem.

Six or eight parents or teachers may be about the right number to allow for the best discussions and interactions. There is some merit in maintaining the same group membership, so that the members will feel free to discuss their problems.

Who Will Lead the Group?

Who will be the leader? If there is a speech and hearing clinician in the community, he will be the logical leader of the group. However, he will need the able assistance of others to help make the discussion groups a success. If there is no speech clinician in the community, someone who has ability to organize, is dependable, and has considerable tact and ability to work with others should be selected as the leader.

Introduction

Discussion meetings are often unsuccessful unless certain rules or principles are observed. It may be worth-while to spend at least one meeting discussing how to conduct effective discussions.

Appointment of Recorder

Someone should be appointed to sum up the main points occasionally, so as to keep the discussion to the point and to record the helpful ideas given by the members of the group. This person could review the meeting for the next session, so as to maintain some degree of unity between the meetings. If questions arise which are not particularly related to the topic of the day's discussion, they should be written down and kept for a later time. The chairman or the appointed member may interrupt the discussion with, "I wonder if that is to the point?"

Some members of the group may need to be encouraged to talk. A question, such as, "Have you had a similar experience?" often stimulates a response. In some cases, the leader may have to insist on allowing every member an opportunity to talk before permitting the "monopolizer" to speak. As much as possible, the permissive atmosphere should be maintained so as to encourage discussion.

Topics for Discussion

The chapter headings of this book may serve as topics for discussion. Specific references and projects are included at the end of each chapter to aid the clinician or leader in planning the discussion meetings. A suggested plan for meetings based on this book will be included in the Appendix. In general, the first part of each period may be spent in the presentation of the factual material; the second half may be used for questions and discussion. Demonstrations, films, and other activities may be used to supplement the discussions according to the time available.

Acknowledgments

This book is divided into three parts: Part I, General Considerations; Part II, Speech Problems; and Part III, Related Factors. Many of the chapters are revisions of articles which appeared in

The Hygeia magazine (*Today's Health,* published by the *American Medical Association*) under the name of Ruth E. Beckey, Ph.D., (Ruth Beckey Irwin) during 1941 and 1942.

Chapters I, VIII, X, and XI are revisions of articles first appearing in *Today's Health*, March, April, May, and June, 1942, respectively. Chapters IV, V, VI, and VII are revisions of articles appearing in August, September, October, and November, 1941, issues of *Today's Health.* Chapters XII, XIII, XIV, and XV are revisions of articles which first appeared in *Today's Health*, September, October, November, and December, 1942, respectively.

The second chapter, "Hear Yourself as Others Hear You," is a revision of an article which appeared in *She* magazine (no longer published) in March, 1943.

Table of Contents

Part One: General Considerations

Chapter 1: Facing the Issue 3
Four Classes of Handicapped Children. Medical Consultants. Need for Mental Hygiene. Summary. Problems and Projects. References. Film.

Chapter 2: Hear Yourself as Others Hear You 11
Voice Quality. Your Pitch. Volume. Rate. Pronunciation. Articulation. Your Speech Enthusiasm. Summary. Problems and Projects. References. Film.

Chapter 3: Learning to Talk 22
First Vocal Response. Babbling Period. Sound-Imitation Period. Language Comprehension Period. Speech and Physical Growth. Special Speech Encouragement. Speech Stimulation. Summary. Problems and Projects. References.

Part Two: Speech Problems

Chapter 4: Speech Disorders 31
Penalties of Inadequate Speech. Adequate Speech—A Miracle. Causes of Speech Problems. Procedures in Diagnosis. When Is Speech Inadequate? Types of Speech Problems. Speech Rehabilitation. Summary. Problems and Projects. References. Films.

Chapter 5: Delayed Speech 41
Causes of Speech Retardation. Early Speech Treatment. Summary. Problems and Projects. References.

Chapter 6: Can the Child Speak Plainly? 49
Norms for Correct Articulation of Sounds. Causes of Sound Errors. Speech Therapy. Summary. Problems and Projects. References. Films. Recordings.

xv

Chapter 7: Children With Stuttering Symptoms 59
　　Physical. Psychological. Sociological. Re-educational. Summary. Problems and Projects. References. Films.

Chapter 8: Children With Cerebral Palsy 68
　　Incidence. Types. Causes. Diagnosis. Therapy. Speech Rehabilitation. Community and National Resources. Summary. Problems and Projects. References. Films.

Chapter 9: Children With Cleft-Palate Speech 76
　　Types. Causes. What to Do? Community Resources. Summary. Problems and Projects. References. Films.

Part Three: Related Problems

Chapter 10: Is He Hard of Hearing? 87
　　Hearing and Speech. Incidence of Hearing Problems. Rehabilitation. Symptoms of Hearing Loss. Treatment Program. Parent Helps Child at Home. The School's Hearing Conservation Program. Medical Follow-up. Educational Follow-up. Summary. Problems and Projects. References. Films.

Chapter 11: Can He Read Well? 102
　　How Many Poor Readers? Speech and Reading. Reading Readiness. Reading Disability — A Penalty. Diagnosis of Reading Problems. Treatment Program. Summary. Problems and Projects. References. Film.

Chapter 12: Personality Adjustment 110
　　Meaning of Personality. Physical Characteristics. Intellectual Factors. Summary. Problems and Projects. References.

Chapter 13: Educational Adjustment 116
　　Education Begins at Birth. What Is Intelligence? Speech and Intelligence. Testing of Intelligence. Levels of Intelligence. Summary. Problems and Projects. References. Film.

Chapter 14: Emotional Adjustment 128
　　Speech Problems and Behavior. Causes of Behavior Problems. Treatment of Emotional Problems. Negativism and Disobedience. Jealousy. Temper Tantrums. Insecurity. Fear. Summary. Problems and Projects. References for Parents. Film.

Chapter 15: Social Adjustment 140
  Personality and Speech. Effect of Speech Inadequacies on Social Acceptance of Child. Cultural Influence Upon Child's Social Personality. Personality Adjustment and Attitudes. Adjustment to Changing Society. Summary. Problems and Projects. References. Film.

Appendices 149

Index 191

Part One

General Considerations

1

Facing the Issue

"My child is not normal" is an admission which is very difficult for most parents. Although the child may have a pronounced defect such as a cleft palate, the parent may not admit the handicap even to close friends. However, the best approach to the problem for both the parent and child is to accept the situation and "make the best of it." To face the problem realistically and constructively will contribute much toward the success of the rehabilitative program.

Four Classes of Handicapped Children

What children are seriously handicapped or differ enough from other children to make adjustments to life very difficult? These children may be classified in four different ways. Perhaps, the most dramatic group is the physically handicapped: the crippled in body, the blind, and the deaf. The crippled refers to those children who have lost arms or legs as the result of accident or disease, to those children who have become crippled as a result of brain injuries or paralysis, or to those children who are extremely weak in health.

The second group of handicapped children may be mentally deficient or unable to compete satisfactorily in educational pursuits with other children. The parent who faces the problem realistically is eager to find the reason for his child's difficulty; he will welcome the cooperation of the school psychologist who can ascertain the assets and liabilities of the child. The results of special tests are interpreted in terms of the child's abilities. A program of activities is planned which provides opportunities for the child to learn according to his abilities. Reducing the chances for failure will add much toward the achievement of happiness and educational growth of the child.

A third group of handicapped children have antisocial behavior. They may lie, steal, fight, or withdraw entirely from any social situation. Sometimes, the child may become so unmanageable that the parent has to seek the aid of some juvenile delinquency officer. Usually, the parents and teachers can adjust most behavior problems before serious consequences result. Parents may, however, refuse to recognize the problem. The child may become uncontrollable. Another type of parent becomes too interested in the child's welfare. Every book on habit formation is read. As a result, the child often tries to evade extreme domination. He resents too much attention! His mother will then wonder, "I can't understand Patty. I have done everything I can to keep her from sucking her thumb, and look at her!" Too much attention! Some parents realize the child will naturally pass through difficult periods, but will not worry too much about them. The child is allowed to find his own way as much as possible. An occasional guiding word or "setting of the stage for good behavior" will in many cases be enough to help the child to become adjusted to difficult situations.

A fourth group of handicapped children may be composed of children with multiple physical, mental, and psychological maladjustments. Under this classification, language disabilities are often found. Speech defects and reading difficulties are the principal problems. For these disorders, the causes are oftentimes overlapping and no one factor may be said to cause a speech defect or reading disability to the exclusion of all others.

Medical Consultants

In the analysis of all four groups of handicaps, the physician is the foremost consultant. Not until he is consulted can the educational director proceed with a program of re-education. There should be close cooperation between medical specialists and parents at all times, particularly in cases of physically handicapped persons. Until quite recently, however, the rehabilitation program of the handicapped individual has been under medical supervision entirely. The necessities of life—food, shelter, and medical service—have been provided. The state and national educational departments have developed facilities for the care of some of the various groups of unfortunate children, but the development of a mental hygiene program for the child and his parents seems to be the most neglected. The child can be well-fed, well-housed, and well-cared for in every way physically, and still remain unhappy. His parents may also be unhappy. Learning to adjust to the handicap and making the best use of physically impaired structures are the goals of parents and child.

Need for Mental Hygiene

"I can't dance like the other girls. What's the use of living?" was the wail of one spastic high-school girl after seeing a beautiful evening gown on one of her girl friends. This girl was beginning to realize that she was different from other girls. As a result, she withdrew from social activities altogether and became dependent on her mother. She was unwilling to accept the reality of her situation. Her mother also added to the problem by accepting a condition which was not real.

How to be happy with a serious handicap is the problem! To be happy, the child must have the right attitudes toward his deficiency. He is not mentally healthy until he is able to adjust himself to his environment with the least friction, and at the same time finds his life highly satisfactory and pleasant. A mental hygiene program for the handicapped child is not essentially different from that for the normal child, since both groups are motivated by the same fundamental human drives. Every child wants to be loved, to belong to someone, to achieve success, to gain approval, and to feel secure, emotionally and economically. He also wants to be physically well. However, since the adjustments to life are often difficult for the handicapped child, he will frequently resort to some defensive mechanism which will help him to escape from the reality of his true condition. He may develop anti-social habits of lying, stealing, negativism, temper tantrums, or daydreaming. He may compensate for his lack of reading ability by drawing or building in the shop. Moreover, instead of admitting his true handicap he may rationalize and blame his backwardness on some other factor.

What should the handicapped child do to make himself happier in his environment? All mental hygiene for the child is based upon his need for security—emotionally, economically, physically, and socially. Certain attitudes and substitute activities may prove valuable to him in his attempt to become adjusted to his handicap. If the substitute activity, however, does not solve the child's particular problem, then that method of adjustment to life becomes entirely undesirable and even harmful.

Most important of all, the child should face the reality of his situation. He must realize that he cannot do some things. He should find the things he can do well and do them! He must learn to accept his limitations, and try not to exceed his physical and mental capacities. The child or adult cannot face his problems realistically unless his family does likewise. Rationalizations or excuses for inferior performances can be avoided by a constructive attitude toward real deficiencies.

Sometimes substitute activities are advisable, so long as the child does not dodge the real problem. For instance, one crippled sportsman resorted to writing a sports column. Compensation in some other field also helps the person to forget his own shortcoming. However, improvement should not be neglected for the development of the substitute field.

Since most of his activities will be with normal people, the handicapped person must learn to live in a normal society. He should feel that he is "normal" in any situation not demanding the use of his special deficiency. For instance, the child without the use of his legs will not be expected to swim or jump with normal playmates, but he may enter intellectual activities with them.

In order to become socially secure, the child needs to develop an attractive personality to offset any unpleasant appearance or effect that he may have. For instance, he should learn how to do several interesting and profitable hobbies. Reading will give information for conversations. Society will often overlook physical defects in a person if that person has achieved a charming and interesting personality. In other words, "What you ARE speaks so loudly, that I do not see your imperfections!"

Courtesy of Hearing and Speech Center of Columbus and Central Ohio.
Speech pathologist counsels with a parent.

Early application of proper mental hygiene for the handicapped child will usually prevent personality maladjustments so often accompanying physical deficiencies. With proper guidance, the defective child can often make happier adjustments to life situations than some of his "normal" playmates.

In addition to helping the child maintain emotional stability, the parents also need to apply some mental hygiene practices to themselves. They need encouragement. In many instances, parents are more unhappy than their handicapped child. They realize what problems life holds for the normal person without any handicaps. What complications are added when the child has to live with a handicap!

The parents' most difficult period occurs when they first realize that their child is different from other children. Emotionally, they are upset so much that they are often unable to help the child who may also be disturbed by his problems. Parents need to be ready to help the child to reorganize his whole life, especially if the affliction has occurred rather suddenly.

The child should be prepared for the difficult periods of adjustment in his life. During adolescence, he will want many things that will be impossible for him to have and unless he is prepared to meet these situations he may grow unhappy and develop some personality problem. He must also be prepared for the period when he will leave the protection of the school and must look for a job. He must know that people will not be too eager to hire him even though he is capable of doing the work as well as his "normal" friends.

Both the child and the parent must face the facts and meet the problems in a constructive way. Failure to recognize the defect may prove harmful to the child. One parent, a superintendent of schools, too, refused to admit that his oldest daughter had a severe hearing loss. He would not allow his wife to send the girl to any special school for treatment. The mother, knowing that the child needed help very badly, finally resorted to divorce before she could have her own way with the handicapped girl.

Parents, also, should try to treat the child as though he were normal. Feeling sorry for him will not help. Some children have grown entirely helpless as the result of too much parental solicitation. The high-school girl, mentioned earlier in this chapter, appeared more crippled than she really was. Her mother waited on her so completely that the girl had developed into a helpless invalid. However, once the mother faced the facts about the true physical condition of the girl, constructive steps were taken. The girl, by readjustments, became independent. The parent should supply the child's wants and needs in much the same way as he does with a normal child.

Summary

Handicapped children may be classified in four ways: (1) physically handicapped, (2) mentally deficient, (3) antisocial, and (4) multiply handicapped. Language disabilities are often found among the children in the fourth classification. However, speech difficulties are often associated with any of the four classes of handicapped children.

A program of rehabilitation involves the cooperation of medical specialists, speech pathologists, educational personnel, and parents.

The more handicapped the child, the more he and his parents need mental hygiene. Facing the issue constructively means to find out about the problem and then do something that will aid the child to compete with his peers as favorably as he is capable. Meeting the problems of the handicapped child realistically is often difficult for parents.

Problems and Projects

1. When was the child's problem most disturbing to you or most difficult to accept?

2. Write an autobiography of your life since a handicapped child has been a part of it.

3. Keep a diary for a week of your activities. Indicate how these activities are affected by your child.

4. Read a life story of a handicapped person who overcame many handicaps because the "issue was faced."

5. Outline constructive steps you can follow in "facing the problem."

References

Baker, L. *Out on a Limb*. New York: Whittlesey House, 1946.

Buck, P.S. *The Child Who Never Grew*. New York: John Day, 1950.

Heiner, M.H. *Hearing Is Believing*. Cleveland: World Publishing, 1949.

Johnson, W. *Because I Stutter*. New York: D. Appleton-Century, 1930.

Leader, P. *And No Birds Sing*. New York: Vanguard Press, 1931.

McDonald, E.T. *Understand Those Feelings.* Pittsburgh: Stanwix House, 1962.

Travis, L.E. and D.W. Baruch. *Personal Problems of Everyday Life.* New York: D. Appleton-Century, 1941.

Tucker, C.D. *Betty Lee:* Care of Handicapped Children. New York: Macmillan, 1954.

Wedberg, C.F. *The Stutterer Speaks.* Redlands, California: Valley Fine Arts Press, 1937.

Film

Your Children and You (Chicago: British Information Services, 39 S. LaSalle Street). Various aspects of parent-child relationships in actual everyday life situations.

2
Hear Yourself as Others Hear You

You spend time and money to make yourself *look* beautiful; but do you ever try to make yourself *sound* beautiful?

You wave your hair, polish your nails, massage your face, or dress yourself in the latest fashions; but do you ever consider your speech or voice? Dirty ragged nails may be unattractive, but so may the woman with the high shrill or rough grating voice. Blotchy, shiny skin may be considered unnecessary, but what about the speech with the "sloppy s" and the protruding tongue? You may be a very attractive person "to look at," but do you "sound" attractive? Even more important than how you appear and sound to others in your social set is how your speech is affecting the speech of children who hear you. Speech is imitated.

Now, what can you do about your speech? Strange as it may seem, no one knows how his voice sounds until he has a record made and can hear it played back. Very seldom does a person recognize his own voice. He usually exclaims, "Is that really my voice?" or "Do I really sound as bad as that?" A little later, he suggests, "What can I do to make my voice sound better? I don't see how my friends have put up with me! I certainly don't want my children to sound like I do."

Maybe, you have no way of hearing yourself as others hear you. Do you have a friend who could record your voice on his new recording machine? Maybe, you could get him to have a frank talk with you as you both listen to your recording. Perhaps, your school has a recording machine and your group could use the machine during one of your afternoon meetings if you are holding parent-discussion meetings. A tape recorder will do just as well, and it usually has higher fidelity than the other

11

type of recorder. Moreover, a tape can be erased and your voice does not become a permanent record.

As you listen to these recordings or playbacks, note whether you sound nasal, hoarse, harsh, shrill, or unpleasant in any way. Next, listen for any carelessness in articulation of sounds. Do you pronounce all of the final *t* sounds and *d* sounds? Do you talk too fast? After a few questions and self-evaluations, you may be able to proceed more intelligently with your speech improvement.

You may be fairly sure that you can profit by some form of speech or voice improvement. According to some college surveys, only about 5 per cent of the population have what is known as excellent speech. All of the rest of the people could probably profit by speech instruction.

Before beginning the improvement of your speech, you will

A teacher listens to a recording of her speech.

Courtesy The Ohio State University.

want to know the characteristics of a good voice. To have good speech and voice, you must have a pleasing voice quality, appropriate pitch for your age and sex, flexibility or variety of inflection, adequate volume for the room in which you are talking, full resonance, good pronunciation and diction, clear-cut articulation, and a certain amount of enthusiasm in your speaking voice.

Voice Quality

Quality is that characteristic of voice which distinguishes you from your friends. That quality may be pleasant or unpleasant. It is your hope that it is pleasant. However, to make certain that your voice will sound pleasing, you may want to do certain exercises which will improve the tones of your speech. If at all possible, it would be advisable to enroll in a class or obtain a teacher who knows how to direct your study.

First of all, you must "think" good tones. Open your mouth and let the tones "roll out." Reading poetry which has many broad vowels will help to give beauty to the voice. For example, "R*o*ll *o*n th*ou* d*ee*p d*a*rk bl*u*e *o*cean," should be spoken with emphasis on the vowels printed in italics.

Relaxation. Relaxation will also help you to acquire that pleasant tone. Some of these exercises will help you to relax the tension about your throat and mouth:

1. Hang your head over and swing it as though you were a rag doll.

2. Standing erectly, let your head pivot on your shoulders without any movement of the body. Let the head roll from right to left as though it were a heavy ball of lead. Twice to the left and twice to the right. This should not be overdone; too much exercise may cause a stiff neck if you are not used to exercising.

3. Lie on your back for a few minutes with eyes closed. Think, "I am quiet; I am relaxing." Think of each part of the body and "let go" each in turn.

4. Push and release the larynx as though you were lifting and dropping a heavy load.

Breathing. Voice quality may also be improved by proper

breath support. In order to have a full voice for speaking, you must speak on expiration. Some people actually try to talk while breathing in the air, or while the air is held. Try some of these breathing exercises:

1. Breathe in for a period of five counts and then breathe out for the same period of time.

2. Breathe in for a count of five and then sigh out for the same length of time.

3. Breathe in and sigh out audibly some word. Continue this until you understand what it is to talk in a controlled manner on the outgoing breath.

4. Try reading this passage pausing for breath at the vertical markings: "He went to town/ to get a new hat/ He found his friend/ who had been to the show/ After shopping/ they went for a ride."

5. Read this passage, observing the pauses: "Speak the speech/ I pray you/ as I pronounced it to you/ trippingly on the tongue/ but if you mouth it/ as many of your players do/ I had as lief the town crier spoke my lines."

Your Pitch

Is your pitch too high or too low? If it is too high, it may sound immature and babyish or whiny. It will be known as a thin voice without much character. If it is too low, you may sound masculine. How can you determine what your optimum pitch should be?

For most speakers, the optimum pitch is likely to be about the fourth or fifth tone above the lowest tone which the person can sing. If the person feels a change of pitch is desirable, guidance from a speech teacher is important. The method used for the attainment of the optimum or best pitch level will depend upon the teacher who is your instructor. Several methods are effective. One of the easiest is the natural method. A moderately deep breath is taken as though preparing for a sigh and then on the outgoing breath, the individual intones "ah." Chant on this pitch level. Ask someone if the pitch level is good for you.

Try the *grunt* technique in which you grunt "ah" or "oh." After getting a tone in this manner, prolong the "ah." Chant some passage or count to 10 on the pitch level attained by the grunt method.

Another method for ascertaining the optimum pitch is through the use of the piano for determining your total pitch range. Start at Middle C, and play down the scale until you reach the lowest note that you can sing and still hear a distinct note. Then sing up the scale until you come to the highest note that you can sing, including the falsetto or "cracked note." Count the number of white keys between the lowest and highest tones. Do this several times to ascertain your accurate number of tones between the lowest and highest notes. Your optimum pitch is probably the fourth or fifth note above the lowest you matched on the piano. Try the pitch level which seems best for you. Let someone else help you to judge. If you find that you are not speaking on your most desirable pitch level, you'll have to practice reading aloud with the "new pitch level" until it seems natural for you.

Flexibility of Pitch. Your voice may sound monotonous. A person, who talks on the same tone, hour after hour, soon tires his listeners. Saying the A,B,C's as though you were mad or with as much variety as possible, may help to give you an idea about how to add more "ups" and "downs" to your speaking voice.

Go to the piano and try singing the scales; then try to put more notes into your speaking voice and at the same time keep the main tones at the level most suitable for you. If you have tried to lower or raise the general pitch level of the voice, you will need to start speaking on the pitch level desired and then add variety in pitch.

Volume

Do you have enough volume in your speaking voice to be understood in any room in which you might wish to speak? Do you use enough breath, or breathe at the right times, to sustain you to the end of your sentences?

Without adequate breath, volume cannot be produced. Volume is not a matter of shouting, for many a person has tried to shout across the footlights with no effect. Resonance, which is the proper production of the sound plus clear articulation, will help the person with adequate breath to push his sounds across the orchestra pit to the rows of people in the theatre. Breathing exercises will also aid the person with the weak voice to attain more control of the volume.

Rate

Do you talk or read so fast that you stumble over your words? You say that you are nervous and cannot help it? Did you ever try talking slower and taking time to breathe frequently? Try it and you will note a sense of power and calmness come over you. Talk slowly and you will find yourself acting slower.

Time your rate of reading! You should not read over 175 or 180 words per minute and if you read slower than 140 words per minute, you are too slow. Of course, you may be unfamiliar with words or hesitate because of other reasons and thereby slow down your speed. If you suffer from breathiness, jerky speech, or dizziness, you are probably reading or talking too fast.

Pronunciation

You may live in the South; you may live in the East; or you may live in the West. The way you pronounce your words will be determined by the speech you have heard. If you were to travel from the East to the West, the Westerner no doubt could tell from which general section you came. He may know that you did not come from Georgia, but could he localize you to a particular section of New York City? If so, your pronunciation should be improved. You will not be considered an entirely cultivated speaker of the English language unless you adopt the pronunciation and diction of the best educated group in your particular area—Eastern, Southern, or general American.

Articulation

Is your speech clear-cut and free from any errors in substitutions, distortions, or omissions of sounds? The consonant sounds are more likely to be defective than are the vowels. Probably the best way to check your own sounds is to secure the cooperation of a friend if no speech teacher is available. Both of you may

Hear Yourself as Others Hear You

sit in front of the mirror and try to say each sound as you discuss it. Only by knowing how sounds are made can you detect your own inaccuracies or judge the errors of your children. Let's classify the consonants according to the manner in which they are produced. In Figure 1, the parts of the mechanism used in the production of sounds are illustrated.

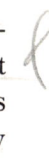

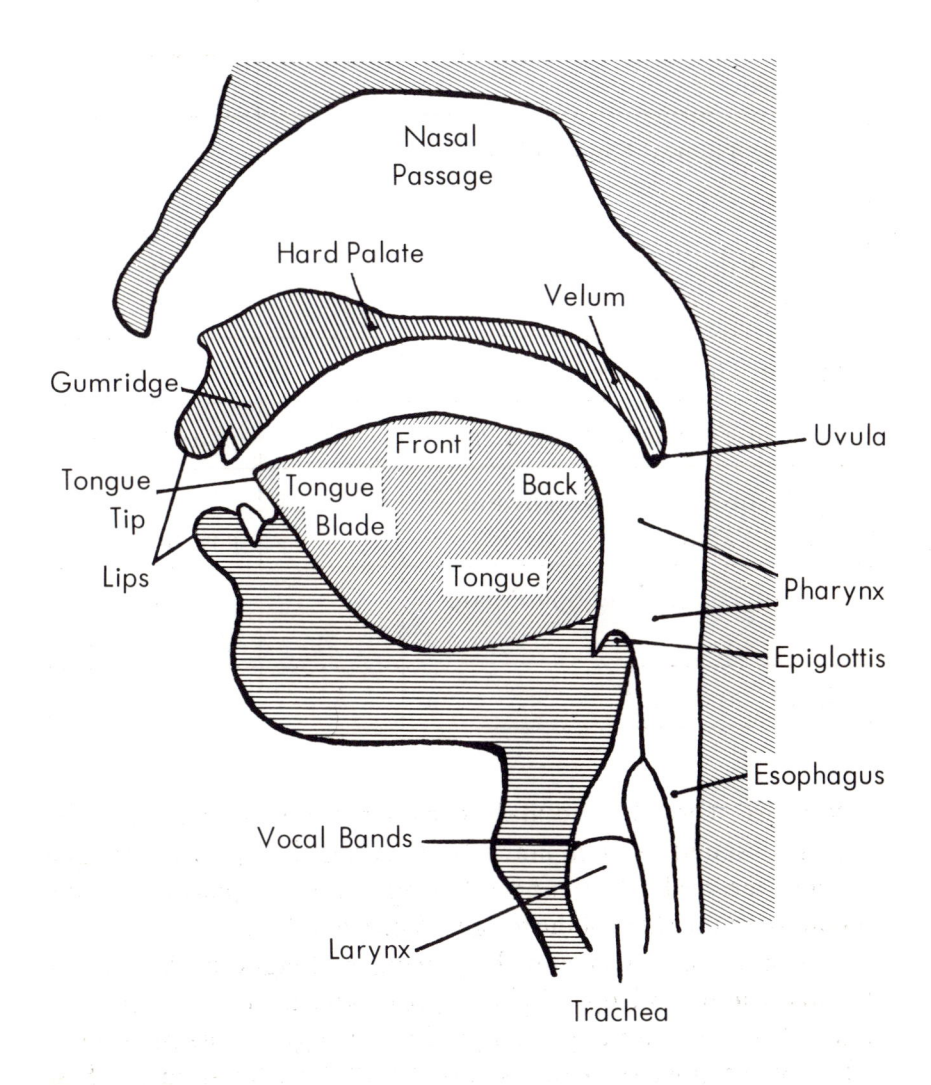

Figure 1. Principal Mechanisms Used in Articulation

Manner and Place of Articulation	Voiceless	Voiced
Lips	*p* *hw*	*b* *m* *w*
Lip-Teeth	*f*	*v*
Tongue Tip and Gum Ridge	*t* *s*	*d* *z* *n* *r* *l*
Tongue Tip and Teeth	*th*	*th*
Blade of Tongue and Hard Palate	*sh*	*zh* as in a*z*ure
Middle or Front of Tongue and Hard Palate		*y* as in *y*ou
Back of Tongue and Soft Palate	*k*	*g* *ng* as in ri*ng*
Glottal (larynx)	*h*	

Now, let's check how to make each of the most difficult sounds:

1. The sound of *l* is made by pressing the tip of the tongue against the teeth ridge and allowing the air to pass out of the mouth over the sides of the tongue. Voice is added.

2. The sound of *s* is made by placing the tongue back of nearly closed teeth and lips slightly spread apart. Air is pushed out against the teeth and lips and produces a slightly hissing sound. The correct position can usually be attained by saying *t* first and holding the position of the tongue after dropping from back

of the teeth. The *z* sound is made just like the *s* except sound or voice is added.

3. The sound of *th* is made by placing the tip of the tongue in spread out position against the inner edges of the upper teeth and blowing air out. Do not let tongue protrude any more than is necessary.

4. The sound of *f* is made by placing the lower lip upward and slightly inward against the edges of the upper teeth. The breath passes out between the lips and the teeth. For the *v* sound, voice is added.

5. The sound of *r* is made by raising the tip of the tongue without touching the teeth or palate and turning it back toward the back of the mouth, leaving a hollow space just above the tip. Voice is added and the *r* sound should be produced. If lips are being rounded in the production of the sound, a simple method to follow is to sit in front of the mirror and watch yourself as you say the *r* sound. Try to say the *r* sound without rounding the lips—smile slightly.

The *s*, *z*, *sh*, and *ch* sounds are often the most difficult sounds for the average person to pronounce correctly or pleasantly. Avoid the protrusion of the tongue for the production of any of these sounds. Again, the mirror is helpful to check yourself on the production of inaccuracies.

Your Speech Enthusiasm

Do you feel free and easy when you talk to your friends, to your club, or to your employer? Do you tense up, close your mouth, and do as little talking as possible?

Perhaps, you are like the college girl taking voice and diction who had at one time worn braces on her teeth and as a result was very sensitive about her mouth. She was quite shy in any speaking situation although she no longer wore any braces. Neither was she aware of the fact that she had developed shyness because of the braces. She had grown accustomed to trying to hide her braces, and so was afraid to smile or to speak. Consequently, her speech was often indistinct and jumbled since she did not open her teeth sufficiently to utter the sounds accurately.

Another girl would not open her mouth widely enough for fear she would talk too loudly. Her mother had called her, "A loud mouth." The girl had withdrawn from speaking situations. Whenever she talked, her mouth was nearly shut.

If you are sure that you can talk as well as anyone else, that your teeth, lips, mouth, and tongue are in good condition, that you can pronounce your words as well as the average person, and that you have no defective sounds, you should feel free and easy in any crowd or in any speaking situation.

With a pleasing voice, clear-cut articulate speech, and an enthusiastic ring in your voice, you should be the attractive speech personality of your crowd as well as the model for your child to imitate.

Summary

No one hears his own voice or speech as others hear him. This means that recordings of speech are necessary if the individual hears the speech inadequacies.

A good voice must be pleasing in quality, have appropriate pitch and intensity, be flexible in variety of pitch and intensity, and be resonant. The speech or articulation should be distinct, not too fast, and free from errors in sound production.

Adequate voice quality is developed through the proper use of breath control, pitch, intensity, and rate of speaking. Freedom from tension is also advisable for the voice which is pleasing.

Pronunciation is often colored by the speech of the section of the country in which the speaker lives. The standard of pronunciation in any general part of the nation is that spoken by the best educated people of the community.

Sounds are classified according to the way they are made: lip, lip-teeth, tip of tongue, tongue-teeth, blade of tongue, and back of tongue. Sounds are also defined as voiceless or voiced. Directions for the production of a few of the most difficult sounds are given in this chapter.

In addition to all of the skills needed for the production of a pleasing voice and adequate articulation, the speaker should have enthusiasm. With practice, speech and voice may be improved.

Problems and Projects

1. Record your speech on a tape recorder so you can hear your speech as others hear you. If you are a member of a class, all persons can record on one tape. When tape is played back, try to identify your own voice.

2. Evaluate your speech from the standpoint of how the voice sounds (pitch, intensity, rhythm, and rate) and how well you articulate. Are you intelligible? Is your voice pleasing in quality? If it is not pleasing, how would you describe your voice?

3. How do you propose to improve your speech and voice? Write a speech improvement program for yourself.

4. Discuss why it is important for a parent or teacher to have good speech.

5. Ask a speech specialist to help you with the diagnosis and treatment of your speech.

6. Refer to the Appendix for materials to use in practicing speech and voice skills.

References

Anderson, V. *Training the Speaking Voice.* 2nd ed. New York: Oxford University Press, 1961.

Dolman, J. *The Art of Reading Aloud.* New York: Harper, 1956.

Eisenson, J. *The Improvement of Voice and Diction.* New York: Macmillan, 1958.

Fairbanks, G. *Practical Voice Practice.* New York: Harper, 1944.

_____. *Voice and Articulation Drillbook.* 2nd ed. New York: Harper, 1960.

Fessenden, A. *Speech and the Teacher.* New York: Longmans, Green, 1946.

Karr, H.M. *Developing Your Speaking Voice.* New York: Harper, 1953.

Sorrenson, F.S. *Speech for the Teacher.* New York: Ronald Press, 1952.

Film

Your Voice (Brooklyn College: Department of Speech), 1950.

3

Learning to Talk

Speech is not inherited! If a child were placed on an island at four months of age with only animals for company, he would not learn to talk. He would communicate his needs in much the same manner as the animals. The child born of American parents in China will learn to speak the Chinese language, unless he is kept in isolation with his parents. Speech is a learned process. A child learns to talk by hearing others talk.

In learning to talk, the child goes through much the same experimentation that the primitive man did. The child gesticulates a great deal to express his wants and dislikes. His most frequent responses are against emotional situations relative to his well-being. As the child matures emotionally, intellectually, and physically, he learns speech according to the stimulations provided by his environment.

When does the baby say his first word? Some mothers will say, "Oh, he said 'mama' and 'papa' when he was about a year old." Of course, some children start talking sooner than others because of more rapid maturation of the nervous system, higher intelligence, or because of certain environmental factors. The average age for beginning to say words is from twelve to fifteen months.

First Vocal Response

The first vocal response of the baby is the birth cry. During the first months almost all of the child's vocal responses are undifferentiated. He cries for everything. No one knows whether the crying means that the baby has pain, is hungry, or whether he wants attention. One may attempt to differentiate the child's specific wants, but such judgment is mainly guesswork.

Babbling Period

From the third to the tenth month, the child begins his vocal play or babbling, which is the source of spoken language. Socialized vocalization by which the child seeks attention, expresses his desires, and resists opposition, usually begins about the fifth month.

Sound-Imitation Period

The sound-imitation, or lallation period, usually begins during the sixth month. The child imitates his own sounds for the pleasure he derives from hearing himself. This period is important in the development of the kinesthetic, or "feel" sense of speech.

Following the lallation period is the echolalic period in which the child imitates the sounds he hears, but does not have any understanding of them. This activity begins about the ninth month.

Language Comprehension Period

The next stage, or the language-comprehension period, occurs long before the child is able to use language with any real facility. He begins to associate words with certain objects. This stage usually starts about the beginning of the second year. At this time, the child needs to receive proper stimulation to encourage his talking.

Happy situations surrounding the child will encourage speech development. The baby learns to talk by associating pleasant experiences with speech situations. When the baby babbles, "papa," "mama," "baba," parents often think, or make themselves believe, that the child is saying his first word. The mother fortuitiously enters the room as her child says "mama." She beams! Her baby has said his first word, so she smiles and perhaps caresses the baby lovingly. Every time the child sees the mother, he says, "mama," as he remembers the previous pleasurable experience. So the child's early speech responses are often conditioned by accompanying happy situations.

According to the reports of 50 mothers, their twelve-months-old-babies' most popular words were "mama," "papa," "bye-bye," and "baby." Some of the other words said by the twelve-months-old-child were "dog," "bow-bow," "ta-ta," "upidee," "kitty," "peek-a-boo," "bread," and "see."

Speech and Physical Growth

Why do some children talk sooner than others? Speech cannot develop until the structures necessary for speech mature, so it can be said that speech develops as the physical growth of the child is made. In many cases, the child who is late in walking may be late in talking. Sometimes, you may have noticed that a child stops talking for a short time while he is learning to do some motor skill, such as crawling or walking. Girls usually mature much more quickly than do boys, and consequently usually start talking sooner. Some authorities maintain that girls should be able to speak all of their sounds correctly by the time they are six; boys need another one and one-half years to catch up with the girls.

Psychologists have found that language and intelligence tend to mature together, each stimulating the other. However, one must not assume that the child is inferior in intelligence just because he is not talking. Other factors may be causing the child's retardation of speech.

Special Speech Encouragement

Since so many factors may be responsible for the delay in the child's development of speech, the child should be given special encouragement in talking. "Why teach the child to talk? He just learns as he does many other things!" That is true! However, the mouth, teeth, tongue, and "voice-box" were not intended for speech. The function of speech is superimposed upon a mechanism used for eating and breathing.

Although the child ordinarily talks without any special effort on the part of his parents or teachers, much can be done to help him to develop speech adequately. Moreover, later difficulties with speech which are often harmful to the child's intellectual, emotional, and social development may be avoided through the skillful "teaching of talking."

Courtesy Cleveland Public Schools.

The clinician stimulates the child by naming each picture several times for the child to hear but with no attempt to have the child respond.

No special speech encouragement should be given before the ninth month outside of repeating the baby's babblings to him. The child likes to hear funny noises and he will smile as nonsense syllables are repeated for him.

To encourage speech development during the speech-readiness period, twelve to thirty-six months, the parents may utilize these various means: (1) the repetition of the baby's babblings, (2) the creation of pleasant situations to accompany the learning of the first words, and (3) the use of short sentences with simple words.

Speech Stimulation

As the child grows older, various types of specific stimulating experiences will do much toward the creation of suitable language responses.

Suitable picture books and toys for the child's age and interest should be provided. Name the objects in the pictures as he looks at them. Be sure to say each word slowly, distinctly, and several

25

times. Wait for a reply, but do not ask for the name of the picture.

Toys should create a desire in the child to express himself. Materials for playing house will often cause him to carry on a monologue. He may act out each family member's part.

Take time to talk with the child. Use short sentences.

It is best for the child to learn words in their natural situations. For instance, he should learn to say, "plate" when he is at the table. You may say to him, "on your plate?" Repeat the word, "plate" several times. Do not ask him to say the word. This procedure provides training in listening for the correct speech pattern. As he learns each new word, he should know what the word *looks* like, *feels* like, *sounds* like, and *does*.

Take trips to the zoo, country, or park. Provide interesting sights and sounds, so that the child will be stimulated to talk. Association with other children will also provide opportunities for speech.

Pleasant home relationships will add to the child's sense of security and thus encourage his desire for communication. By encouragement and praise, you can do much to make the child independent, secure, and expressive.

Summary

The ability to talk is learned from hearing others talk. Sometimes, the learning process is hindered by physical or environmental factors.

The average child learns to talk in several sequential steps: (1) first vocal response at birth, (2) vocal play and babbling, (3) sound imitation or lallation period, (4) language comprehension period, and (5) meaningful speech.

Children should be encouraged to talk through the repetitions of the baby's babblings, development of pleasant situations to accompany speech, and use of one-word sentences until the child begins to talk. Talking to the child, with many repetitions of the word, will serve to stimulate speech development. Trips and play activities to build up a vocabulary of meaningful words are useful also to stimulate communication.

Problems and Projects

1. Read and review a case history of a child delayed in speech who learned to talk. Observe the techniques used.
2. Write a case history of your own child's speech development.
3. Demonstrate for the class how to teach speech to a child without calling attention to his speech inadequacy.
4. Read and report on one of the references at the end of this chapter.
5. Visit a speech stimulation class for pre-school children. Write a report of your observations.

References

Anderson, V.A. *Improving the Child's Speech.* New York: Oxford University Press, 1953.

Beasley, J.E. *Slow to Talk:* A Guide for Teachers and Parents of Children With Delayed Language Development. New York: Columbia University, Teachers College, Bureau of Publications, 1956.

Berry, M.F. and J. Eisenson. "The Normal Development of Speech." *Speech Disorders.* New York: Appleton-Century-Crofts, 1956, Chap. 3.

Irwin, R.B. "Speech Comes to a Five-Year-Old Boy." *Journal of Speech Disorders,* XI (1946), 197–203.

Johnson, W., et al. "Retarded Speech Development." *Speech Handicapped School Children.* New York: Harper, 1956, Chap. 6.

Van Riper, C. *Teaching Your Child to Talk.* New York: Harper, 1950.

Part Two

Speech Problems

4

Speech Disorders

Only five persons out of every 100 have excellent speech! This has been the estimate made by several investigators as a result of surveys made in school systems. At the other extreme, from 5 to 10 per cent have defects severe enough to need the services of a speech specialist. Consequently, approximately 95 per cent of the people could use varying degrees of speech improvement. In Figure 2, the degrees of speech adequacy are represented through the use of a "normal" curve. In this chapter, we will be concerned about the 8 per cent labeled "Clinical."

Even though the main responsibility for speech improvement lies with the educational systems, the parents need to know some of the facts related to speech since the important speech developmental period occurs during the pre-school age. The parent must be able to recognize the first indications of a speech disorder, to have some idea how to encourage a better development of speech, and to know what factors in the child's environment or health may not be conducive to good speech.

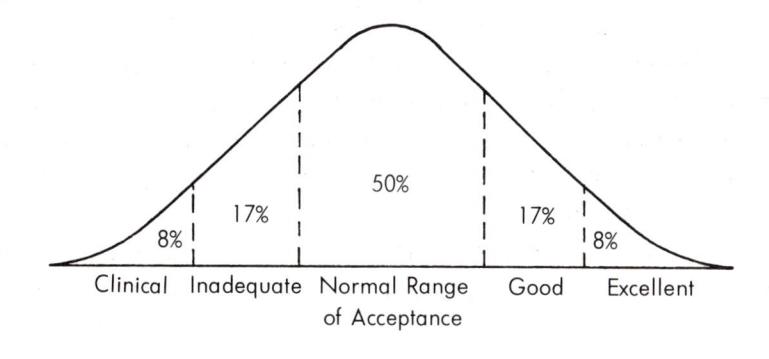

Figure 2. Relative Degrees of Speech Adequacy

Penalties of Inadequate Speech

If the child stutters, or has some severe articulatory deviation, his happiness and success in school and work may be affected if the disorder is not corrected at an early age. The older he grows, the more handicapping the speech inadequacy becomes. In society, the speech-handicapped person will remain silent frequently rather than to be made the object of stares and ridicule. As adolescence approaches, and the boy or girl becomes interested in his appearance and the opposite sex, he finds his affliction harder to bear. Then as he approaches time to get a job, the speech handicap becomes an economic problem. An employer may not want to hire a person who stutters excessively, especially if the prospective employee will have much occasion to deal with people. Consequently, many opportunities may be closed to the person with a speech disorder. He may not be able to teach; he may not be able to clerk in stores; he may not preach; and he may not be able to be a doctor, lawyer, or salesman. He may be placed in some lonely job where his contact with people is at a minimum.

In many cases, the speech deviate is retarded educationally because of his disorder. The student who stutters or has unintelligible speech may not volunteer information. He often sits and lets his classmates do the talking. The teacher, thinking that the child does not know the answer, frequently grades him accordingly.

Before permanent injury is done to the child educationally, psychologically, socially, and economically, the aid of a speech specialist should be secured as early as the child is found to be retarded or irregular in his speech development. The mother may be comforted by the family physician, friends, or relatives with "Oh, don't worry; he'll outgrow it." Cases are often cited of children who were slow in learning to talk or used baby-talk until six years of age. It may be true that some do outgrow the difficulty, but many do not.

To the average person, varying degrees of poor voices and speech, seriously handicapping personality and indirectly handicapping professional advancement, are given little consideration. The sales girl behind the notion counter in the dime store may have a whining, nasal voice; a housewife may not be welcome at the women's club because of her high, shrill voice; a school teacher may have a raspy, hard, harsh voice which irritates her pupils after 10 minutes; or the business man may lisp and talk with "mush in his mouth." These people can not usually hope to be promoted professionally or socially.

Adequate Speech—A Miracle!

When the extreme complexity of the speech organs involved in speaking is considered, it is a wonder that anyone speaks well at all. Biologically and fundamentally, no part of the human organism was intended primarily for speech. The breathing mechanism is used to help supply air to the lungs so life may be maintained. The larynx or the voice-box serves two main functions: (1) to regulate the amount of air going to and from the lungs, and (2) to prevent any small substance or gaseous element from entering the trachea. The organs used in articulation (teeth, tongue, throat, lips) are primarily intended for the ingestion, mastication, and swallowing of food. So speech has been a development super-imposed upon a mechanism already organized for bodily functions.

Causes of Speech Problems

Since speech is an "overlaid" function, the growth of good speech is often slow and defective. Any malfunctioning of a part of the so-called speaking mechanism will interfere with adequate speech responses. Poor breath control often occurs in stuttering, nervous-rapid speech, and various voice disorders. A defective larynx, or the improper functioning of the vocal folds, will often cause aphonia (complete lack of voice) or a very hoarse voice.

A child may be incapable of producing a good t or d if his frenum is so short that the tongue cannot reach the ridge just behind the upper teeth. The tongue-tied condition is illustrated in Figure 3.

Harelip and cleft palate are defects of the articulatory organs that must be repaired by surgery before any speech work can be done. An injury to the speech areas of the brain during birth, or during childhood by accident or by disease, may affect the ability to speak. Even the functioning of the ear is important to

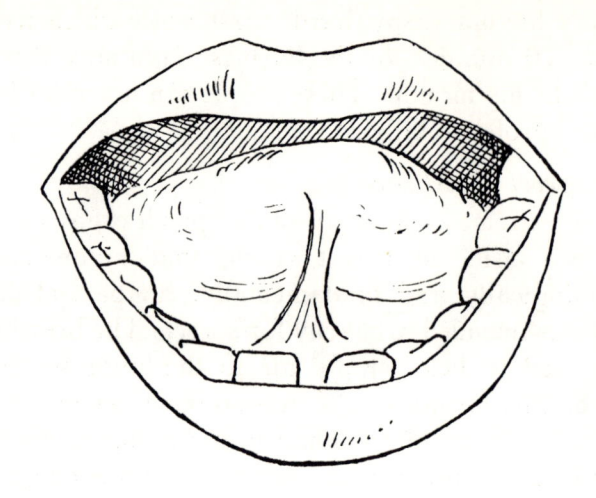

Figure 3. Tongue Tie

speech acquisitions. Without hearing, speech cannot be heard, and consequently not learned. The physician must determine the structural adequacy of the speech organs. Until certain organic defects have been removed or repaired, no speech re-education can profitably take place.

If the physical condition of the speech mechanism is in perfect condition, the parent or teacher should check the child's psychological and environmental influences. The child may feel insecure as a result of continual friction between his parents or he may not be receiving proper speech stimulation.

Possibly, speech does not mature as rapidly or accurately as one expects because the mentality is too low. If low mentality is suspected, a reliable psychologist should be consulted. However, many children with no speech, or with unintelligible speech, are unable to give any fair indication of their intelligence. Therefore, if the child is under six years of age, and appears bright in his activities, some speech training should be given. At least a trial period may be advisable to ascertain whether the child can profit by instruction.

Speech Disorders

Hereditary factors may affect the development of speech in some cases. It is believed that, possibly, certain weak physiological and nervous structures may be inherited that are not conducive to the development of good speech. These mechanisms may be more susceptible to injuries, diseases, or shocks which seem to produce speech disorders in some children, but not in others.

Procedures in Diagnosis

What general procedure should be taken with children who have speech disorders? Since every speech case differs, no one set of rules can be set for all. A speech pathologist, if available, should be consulted for guidance in making diagnosis and referrals. If advised by the speech pathologist, a reputable physician should be asked to determine if any organic defects exist to cause the speech inadequacy.

The child's physical and psychological environment should also be studied for possible disturbing factors. Has anyone used baby-talk with the child? Has there been excessive quarreling in the home? Is distinct speech used? Are the parents too busy to talk to the child? A psychologist may help to determine the environmental elements unsatisfactory for the best speech development.

When Is Speech Inadequate?

Speech or voice may be seriously inadequate when the individual is incapable of securing adequate social responses and thereby attracts attention to himself. A speech specialist may be needed to diagnose the causes of the speech problem, but the parent or teacher can usually point out the severe stutterer, lisper, or the conspicuously inarticulate speaker.

Sometimes other problems are confused with speech difficulties. The child's inability to read may be reflected in the hesitancies of oral reading; the use of improper grammar or incorrect pronunciation are not to be confused with speech problems; inadequate preparation of assignments may make the oral recitations appear to be related to speech problems; certain types of personality maladjustment may be confused with speech problems. The "shy" child often talks with inadequate volume or not at all.

Mental retardation is another condition which is often related to speech problems. Children with low mentality often have speech inadequacies. However, not all children with speech problems are necessarily expected to be low in mentality.

If the related problem were eliminated, would the child still have a speech problem? If so, speech therapy should be provided.

Types of Speech Problems

In Chapters V through IX, the following speech problems are considered: delayed speech, articulatory deviations, stuttering, speech problems associated with cerebral palsy and cleft palate. In Chapter X, some attention is given to the speech problems associated with the hard-of-hearing condition.

Delayed Speech. Delayed speech is determined by comparing the speech development of the child with the norms of expected development for a particular age. Children are usually expected to say their first words at the age of twelve to fifteen months and two-word sentences beginning at ages eighteen months to two-and-one-half years. Children are expected to vary considerably in the beginnings of speech and still fall within the normal range of speech development. However, any child who does not speak by the age of three years should be taken to a speech pathologist for guidance. Oftentimes, the speech specialist can give helpful suggestions for parents to follow in the home. Referrals to other specialists may also be necessary.

Delayed speech and language development may be evidenced by complete lack of speech, babbling continued beyond the usual age, delay in speaking first words or sentences, unintelligible speech, and inadequate sentence length or amount of speech.

Articulatory Problems. Articulatory problems are represented by omissions, substitutions, and distortions of sounds. Certain sounds may be habitually omitted from words, such as *l* in "dollar" which may become "dow-ar." "*Wun*" is a common substitution for "*run*." The *s* sound is often distorted by whistling, hissing, or mushiness. About 80 per cent of the children enrolled in the case loads of public-school speech clinicians have problems in articulation.

Stuttering. Stuttering is a disturbance in the rhythm of speech usually characterized by repetitions of sounds, syllables, phrases, or by complete stoppage of speech. The speech problem is often accompanied by unnecessary eyeblinks, facial grimaces, and bodily movements. About six to ten children out of every 1000 school children may have symptoms of stuttering.

Speech Problems Associated With Cerebral Palsy and Cleft Palate. Speech problems associated with cerebral palsy and cleft palate are usually described in terms of articulation, voice, and rhythm. **Cleft-palate** speech is principally characterized by nasality and inadequacies in the production of plosive sounds like *p, b, k, g, t, d.* Any sound which requires air pressure, such as the *s,* may also give difficulty to the child with an inadequate palate.

The child with cerebral palsy will often have slow, labored speech which may be characterized by monotony and sound deviations due to incoordination of muscles used in speech production.

Voice Problems. Voice problems are usually classified as disorders of pitch, loudness, and quality. The pitch may be too high or too low; the voice may be too loud or too soft; the quality is unpleasant or pleasant. If unpleasant, the voice may be described as raspy, thin, strident, harsh, hoarse, or nasal.

Only two children out of every 1000 are estimated to have voice problems. In the case load of the school clinician, 4 per cent of the children have inadequate voices.

Understanding something about the care of the child's voice is important for both parents and teachers. Misuse of the voice during illness or screaming excessively in play may lead to irritated vocal folds. Some of the voice problems are associated with colds, laryngitis, enlarged adenoids, or hearing difficulties.

When the child has a noticeable voice problem, the services of the speech pathologist should be sought. In many instances, referral to a medical specialist for laryngeal examination will be made.

The parent and teacher need to have good voices themselves

in order to serve as models for children to imitate. In some instances, children have been found to have the same types of voices as a parent. In order to assist the parent or teacher in the improvement of voice, Chapter II is included in this book.

Speech Rehabilitation

Action toward the eradication of the speech disorder should be started as soon as possible. Every year of delay beyond four or five years of age will add to the difficulty of correction as well as to the possible personality maladjustments of the child.

Good health is essential to the child who has speech difficulties. Relaxation, proper exercise and rest, adequate diet and regularity of meals, sufficient sleep, and cleanliness are all important for the maintenance of the best health.

Speech Therapy: Stimulating speech responses.

Courtesy The Ohio State University.

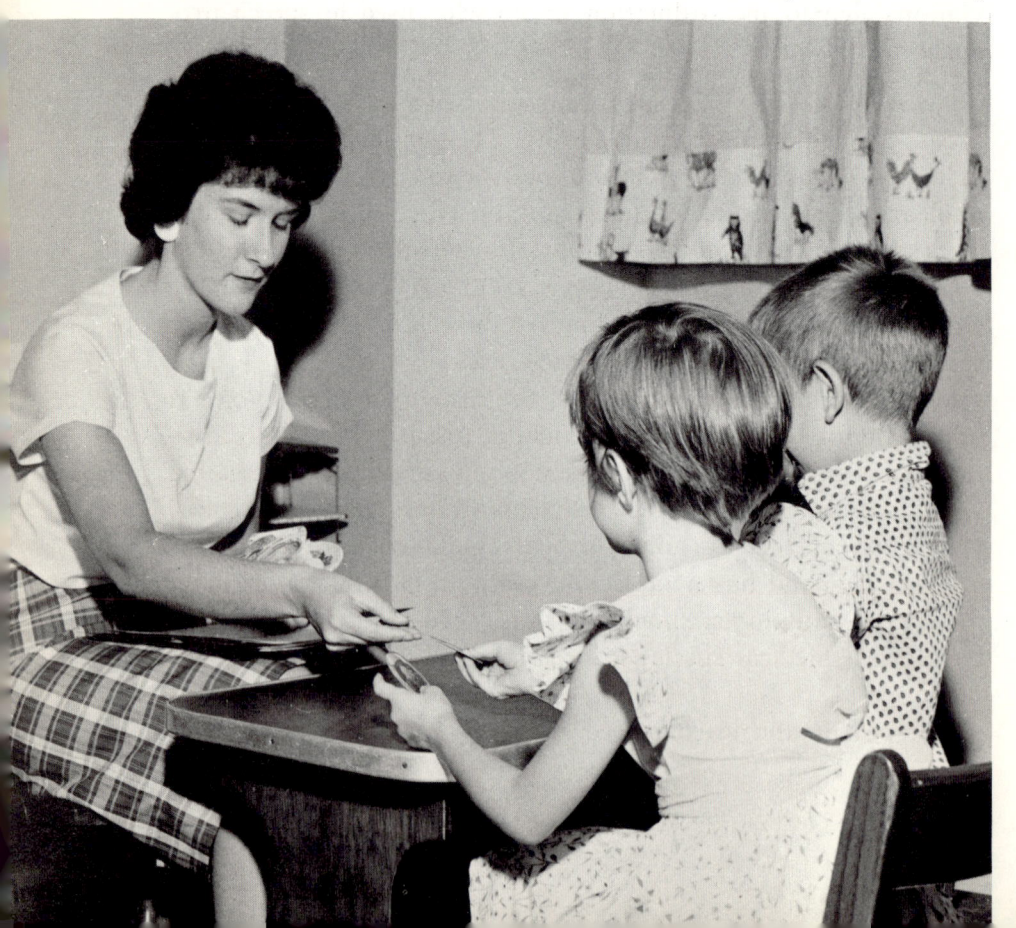

Actual re-education of the seriously speech-handicapped child will need to be handled by the speech specialist in cooperation with other professional personnel. If no qualified speech pathologist is available in the community, the parents or teacher should seek someone at the nearest university speech and hearing clinic.

Summary

From 5 to 10 per cent of the school children have speech problems serious enough to need the help of a speech pathologist. The child who stutters, substitutes sounds, speaks inaudibly, or does not talk at all is severely penalized in his associations with other persons. Grades may be affected because he does not recite or because no one can understand him when he does recite.

Speech problems may be caused by organic factors, such as a defective larynx, palate, lips, or tongue. Lack of hearing may also affect speech, since speech is learned by hearing it. Usually, the majority of speech problems are due to poor learning conditions or some psychological factor. Mentality may also be associated with speech adequacy.

In diagnosis and treatment, the services of a qualified speech pathologist and other professional persons may be needed. The parents may be asked to supply information so that adequate diagnosis and treatment may be accomplished.

Speech is inadequate when it calls attention to itself, may cause the possessor to withdraw from speaking situations, and interferes with the communicative process. The types of speech difficulties are usually classified as disorders of voice, articulation, rhythm (stuttering), and language (speech retardations). Problems associated with cerebral palsy, cleft palate, and the hard-of-hearing condition usually are characterized by disorders of articulation, voice, and rhythm. Aphasia or disorder of language may be associated with the cerebral palsied condition.

Speech rehabilitation for the speech-handicapped person needs to be done under the guidance of qualified speech specialists whenever possible.

Problems and Projects

1. What are your nearest resources for speech examinations?
2. What can you do if no speech specialist is available in your community?
3. What do you think caused your child's speech difficulty?
4. Review a film on speech disorders.
5. Visit a speech class for speech-handicapped children in your schools or at the university. Write a report of your observations.

References

Johnson, W., ed. *Speech Problems of Children.* New York: Grune and Stratton, 1950.

Johnson, W., et al. *Speech Handicapped School Children.* New York: Harper, 1956.

Van Riper, C. *Speech Correction.* New York: Prentice-Hall, 1954.

Films

These Untrained Tongues (Creative Graphics, University of Denver).

Introduction to Speech Problems (Detroit: Wayne State University Audio-Visual Department).

5

Delayed Speech

Perhaps the child is slow to talk. If he is past two-and-one-half or three years of age and does not have adequate speech or any speech at all, then the advice of some speech specialist should be sought. The average child is putting words together in sentences by the time he is less than two years old.

Instead of using speech as a means of securing an object of his desire, the child with delayed speech uses gestures and noises. Asking for a drink of water becomes a jerky gesture toward the sink accompanied by an urgent grunting noise. If the delay continues beyond thirty-six months, the child may develop extreme negativistic attitudes and refuse any help that might develop his speech.

Betty was the seven-year-old daughter of two physicians. She was a beautiful child with seemingly normal intelligence, although an accurate check on the intelligence of non-speaking children is impossible. Her only word was "bye-bye," which is often the first word of a twelve-months-old baby. Betty was making all of the sounds necessary for speech in her babbling noises made during play. She could carry tunes easily. Her case history showed no particular factor which might have caused her trouble. She was a strong-willed child whose mother was quite the opposite type. Since the parents did not bring Betty to the clinic during the speech readiness period, a strong aversion toward speech activity had developed. Betty made no attempt to cooperate with her instructors. Instead, she deliberately resisted their efforts. Her parents had waited too long to seek speech help.

Children without speech like attention, but certainly not the attention that will necessitate speech responses. Imagine some kind, interested person asking a speechless child, "What is your name?"

Parents should guard against making the speech difficulty worse by unnecessary comments about the child in his presence, or making the child feel any more inferior than he already does. The more intelligent the child, the more will he sense his handicap.

Causes of Speech Retardation

Many factors may have been responsible for the child's delay in speech development. No one factor can be said to be more important than any other. Jimmy may have had a severe birth injury which was responsible for his slow or inadequate development; Mary may have been severely frightened at the time she was beginning to learn speech; or John may have had some severe disease during his speech-learning period. What causes delayed speech in one child will not cause it in another. Furthermore, three or more disturbing factors are necessary to cause the average case of speech retardation.

The usual reason given by many authorities for delayed speech is mental deficiency. However, parents need not conclude that their child is mentally deficient to the exclusion of all the other possible factors affecting the child's inadequacy in speech. Investigations have revealed that the ability to reveal intelligence often increases after the child has begun to talk.

If the child has poor motor control, an injury to the central nervous system may be suspected. Prolonged labor during birth of the child may have caused some brain damage.

In addition to possible cerebral birth injuries, various lesions of the brain and nervous system may have occurred as a result of some severe infectious disease. Of all the diseases, measles appears more frequently among children with delayed speech than normally speaking children. Measles may cause lesions in various parts of the neural structures.

Although no significant findings have been made in regard to handedness and delayed speech, the child with no speech tends to lack hand preference. Since speech is supposed to be a function of the dominant hemisphere of the brain (right side for left-handed people, and left side for right-handed people), the early establishment of a hand preference is expected to lead to greater language facility.

Parents often anticipate the wants of a child in such a way that the child feels no need for speech. He succeeds in having all of his needs fulfilled through the use of numerous gestures and grunts. The mother and father are pleased with this type of expression and feel that the child is a "cute little actor." The continuation of such practice, however, delays speech development.

Sometimes, children are slow with speech development because they associate too much with children of their own age. Children usually learn language from persons older than themselves. Twins are often delayed in speech as they are together too much without the beneficial effect of older children who have more mature speech. The same may be said of children who are about the same ages.

In one family, the three children ranged in ages—four, three, and two. Since the family lived in the country, and the parents were too busy to spend much time with the children, the three small children invented a language of their own. The oldest child acted as the "boss," directing the younger children what to do and how to do it. Outsiders were often amused at the busy activities of the children, but understood none of their language. To some, this type of language was called "pig Latin." As the children grew older, the mother became alarmed because no one could understand them. The oldest girl was sent home by the teacher because her speech was unintelligible. However, with particular instruction from the mother, the child soon learned to talk.

The famous Dionne quints may have suffered somewhat from their close association with one another. However, their prematurity made them retarded in motor development and consequently made them slow in language development. As with other small children, the "quints" depended a great deal upon the efficiency of their gestures. The sisters seemed to understand one another's acting very well. Moreover, because of their frailness, many of their human needs were satisfied before they could give any form of communication. However, the quints took a sudden spurt in talking just before their third birthday. They had 110 words at the age of three, and 90 per cent of the words were learned during their thirty-sixth month. Their first words were "mama," "papa," "tantan," "dotteur," and "tittat."

Early Speech Treatment

Prevention of speech disorders is as important as prevention of diseases, and should be studied by parents, teachers, and physicians. If possible, one should prevent the speech difficulty through the occurrence of causes. If prevention is impossible, then early treatment is extremely important, especially with speech-retarded children.

If the child does not develop speech by the age of two-and-one-half or three years with some encouragement, no time should be wasted before seeing a speech specialist. A delay may mean that the child will never learn to talk, that he may have some difficulty in learning speech, or that he may develop unintelligible speech or some unfavorable personality traits.

The three methods of approach for the treatment of the speechless child are through the auditory, visual, and kinesthetic senses. The child must be able to hear speech, to see speech, and to feel speech. Any physical inadequacy in any of these three areas will delay the child in learning speech at the normal age.

Through what is known as the stimulus-response method, the child is stimulated by the parent or teacher who repeats the correct sound or word several times. The child is expected to respond with some attempt at saying the sound; however, the speechless child may only listen and begin to build associations between the spoken word and the object. For instance, a ball is picked up by the child. The mother may say, "ball, ball, ball." She looks at the child and says "ball" again. If the child grunts something in his attempt to say "ball," the mother should feel rewarded. In no instance, should the mother or teacher say, "Now you say 'ball' for Mommie." It is enough to give the correct auditory stimulation for the child. In time, the child may surprise you with the correct response.

An excellent time for the use of the stimulus-response technique is during the story or picture book period. As the child points to

Courtesy The Ohio State University.
Individual Speech Therapy: Using pictures to stimulate speech.

the picture, the mother may say the name of the picture several times, but with no attempt at getting the child to respond. It is hoped that this procedure, if followed patiently by the parents, will finally result in speech responses by the child.

The auditory stimulation method is often supplemented by the visual method when the teacher directs the attention of the child to her face as she says the sounds. This works very well for the visible sounds. Using the stimulus-response method in front of a mirror also calls attention to the way sounds are made.

Entirely speechless children have responded quite favorably to the moto-kinesthetic treatment, in which the clinician applies her hands to the organs of articulation to show just where the speech mechanisms are to be placed in order to say the sound or word correctly. For instance, to direct the saying of the word, "ball," the clinician places her fingers both below and above the lips in a spread-out manner and then presses the two lips together. While she does this, the word "ball" is produced audibly.

The teachers of the deaf have to rely on the kinesthetic method to a great extent to supplement the visual cues of speech. The use of the back of the hand to feel the breath used in k or t helps the child to sense the difference between the k and t sounds and those which require voice such as the d and g sounds.

Therapy for the speechless or inarticulate child has only been suggested here. The careful guidance of a speech specialist is needed. The parent can help by preventing factors which add to the delay in speech development and by encouraging the child to talk during the speech readiness period (eighteen months to two-and-one-half years).

Parents may help children to talk by encouraging them to imitate sounds found in the city or country, or by stimulating them

A child with retarded speech is often more responsive at the playhouse. Indirect therapy is used when the child is shy.

Courtesy The Ohio State University.

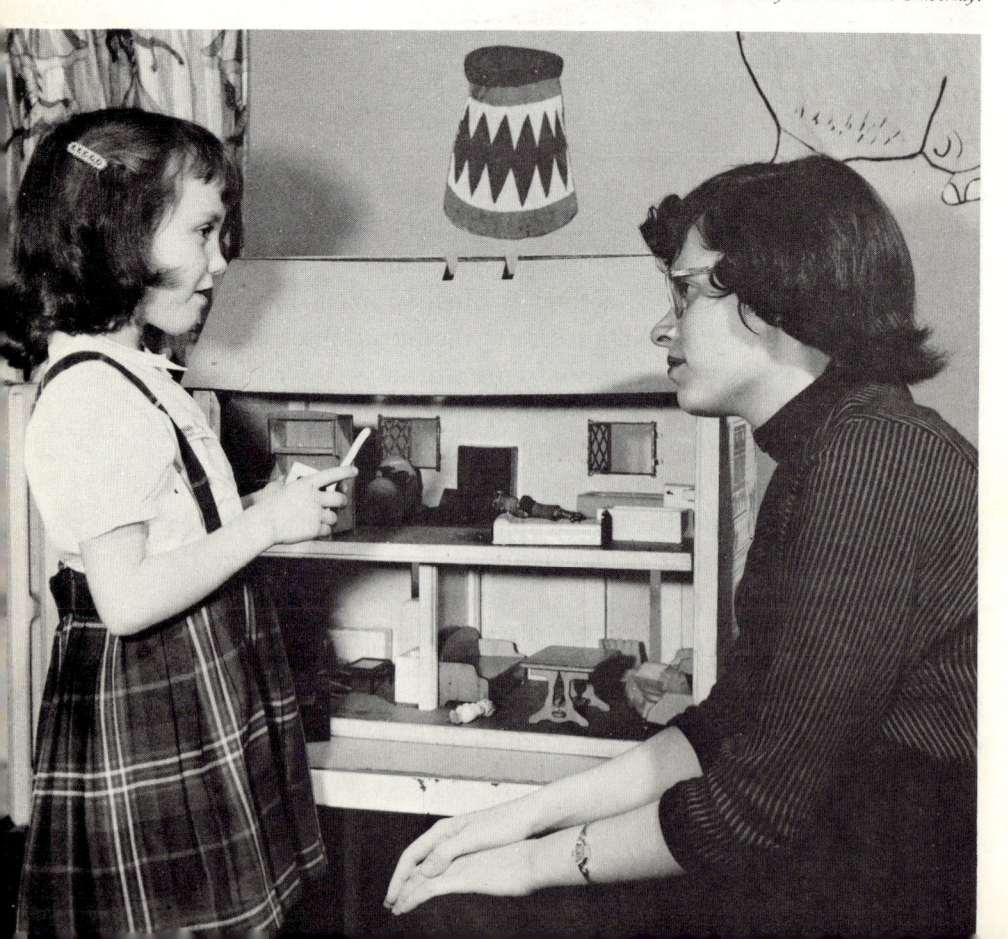

with the words as they play with objects for which the words are names. As children play, they are more likely to use vocal equipment. The use of some rhythmical syllables or words over and over may cause the child to respond. *Mother Goose's Nursery Rhymes* or other rhythmical poetry should be read frequently to develop sound patterns.

Talking in short phrases with many repetitions is indicated for the child who is slow to talk. Talking slowly and in short phrases by the parent gives the child a model which he might be expected to hear and so imitate as he is able.

Summary

Children who have not learned to talk during the speech readiness period (eighteen months to two-and-one-half years) may be slow to talk unless they have some special help from parents and specialists in speech pathology. Children without speech usually resort to a gesture language and may keep this form of communication if the need for speech is not felt.

Many factors may cause the delay in speech development. Anticipation of the needs of a child is a very common cause. The child may feel no need for speech. A stimulating speech environment needs to be provided for the child, so that adequate communication through speech will result. The speech clinician usually appeals to the sense avenues of audition, vision, and kinesthesia in the development of speech adequacy.

Problems and Projects

1. What may cause speech retardations?
2. Cite a case of delayed speech. What contributed to the slow development?
3. Observe a group of speech-retarded children who are receiving speech therapy. Report on the procedures used in therapy.
4. How does the treatment of "shy" children with speech problems differ from older children?
5. When is speech delayed or retarded?

References

Backus, O. and J. Beasley *Speech Therapy With Children.* Boston: Houghton Mifflin, 1951.

Irwin, R.B. "Speech Comes to a Five-Year-Old Boy." *Journal of Speech Disorders,* XI (1946), 197—203.

Matthews, J., E.J. Burgi, J.W. Birch, and E.R.P. Wade. *The Best Speech Series.* Pittsburgh: Stanwix House, 1960.

Strazzulla, M. "A Language Guide for the Parents of Retarded Children." *American Journal of Mental Deficiency,* LIX (1954), 48—58.

Van Riper, C. *Teaching Your Child to Talk.* New York: Harper, 1951.

Zedler, E.Y. *Listening for Speech Sounds.* New York: Harper, 1955.

6

Can the Child Speak Plainly?

Does he say "tat" for "cat" or "din" for "green"? Is the child a speech defective just because he substitutes a few sounds?

"Oh, he'll outgrow it. I never heard a child who didn't make some mistakes," is a common reaction to children's speech inaccuracies. That is true. One must expect certain irregularities in a young child's early speech just as the child may be expected to stumble and fall while he is learning to walk. Since the speech mechanism is complicated, it is remarkable that the child learns to talk as soon or as well as he does.

Many sounds are difficult to distinguish. For instance, the *m* and *n* sounds are very much alike and may be confused if the child does not observe lip movements carefully. Hearing the difference between the *f* and the *th* as used in "thin" is also difficult. Added to this problem of the similarities between some of the sounds is the possible sound deviations which an adult in the home may use. The German grandmother may be using a *d* sound for the *th* sound, making "mother" sound like "mudder." The patterns of speech which the child hears have a great effect upon how he speaks. A child usually learns to speak what he hears in his home.

Norms for Correct Articulation of Sounds

What deviations are expected or considered "normal" in the child's early speech development? Some idea of what to expect may be obtained from the research of Davis, Poole, and Templin. In the study by Davis[1] of children between the ages of five and ten, 56 per cent of the boys and 73 per cent of the girls had per-

---

1. E.A. Davis, "The Development of Linguistic Skill in Twins, Singletons With Siblings, and Only Children From Ages Five to Ten Years," (Minneapolis: University of Minnesota Press).

TABLE I	Norms for the Production of Sounds	
Age	Poole's Norms	Templin's Norms
3		*m, n, ng, p, f, h, w*
3-1/2	*b, p, m, w, h*	*y*
4		*k, b, d, g, r*
4-1/2	*d, t, n, g, k, ng, y*	*s, sh, ch*
5-1/2	*f*	
6		*t, th, v, l*
6-1/2	*v,* voiced *th* as in *th*at, *sh, l,* a*z*ure	
7		*th* as in *th*at, *z*, *zh* as in a*z*ure, *j*
7-1/2	*s, z, r, th* as in *th*in, *wh*	

fect articulation at the age of five-and-one-half years; 87 per cent of the boys and 95 per cent of the girls had perfect articulation at nine-and-one-half years.

Poole[2] found that children who were physically and mentally normal may be expected to articulate all of the sounds accurately by the age of eight. Boys were slower to reach maturity than were the girls, who could articulate all of the sounds accurately by the age of about six-and-one-half years. The boys were able to say their sounds correctly about a year later.

In a study of 480 children, Templin[3] found that 75 per cent of the subjects correctly produced the consonant as indicated in Table I. As will be noted by comparing the norms of Templin's 480 children with Poole's 65 children, there are some discrepan-

---

2. I. Poole, "Genetic Development of Articulation of Consonant Sounds in Speech," *Elementary English Review,* II (1934), 159—161.

3. M.C. Templin, *Certain Language Skills in Children* (Minneapolis: University of Minnesota Press, 1957).

cies. However, the two sets of norms will serve as guides for the parent or teacher who wonders at what age the child is normally expected to say sounds correctly. The knowledge that the three-year-old child is not abnormal if unable to say "strawberry" tends to relieve the anxiety of the parent.

All of the sounds such as *p*, *b*, *m*, *t*, and *d* which are easily seen when produced cause the least difficulty for the child. Substitutions are usually made for the back sounds *k*, *g*, *ng*, *l*, *j*, and *r* because the tongue positions are not easily seen. Consequently, "tat" may be heard for "cat," or "din" for "green," since the sounds substituted are easily seen and present a similar explosive sound.

If the child continues to make substitutions and omissions after the age of five, the parent may conclude that the child may need some help with his speech. Although Poole's and Templin's norms of sound development indicate that efficiency in sound production may not be expected until certain ages, there is no reason why the children cannot eliminate inaccuracies with a little help. Such help given without calling attention to the fact that it is a "speech defect" may prevent teasings from children at school or on the playground.

Simply saying the word two or three times for the child without asking him to repeat after you will help him to hear the correct pattern. If this procedure is followed, the child may start to repeat the sound or word after you. The essential practice for the parent to avoid is asking the child to say the sound. Merely repeating the word so the child can hear it is enough. Correction and attention called to speech inadequacy will only add to the problem and delay the improvement of the speech.

A beautiful five-year-old girl, who had practically all of the speech substitutions and omissions that were possible, came to the speech clinic. She was an only child who had received too much attention in the home. Her parents enjoyed using baby-talk with her. As a result, this young "glamor" girl was quite infantile in her speech growth. She would say, "me don't know." Her speech responses contained no *w*; *f* became *s*, *p*, or *t*; and *s* was *t*; the word "green" was "din," and "red" was "e;"

"fish" was "pish," and "wagon" was "agon." However, she was not yet aware of her inadequate speech.

Another child, who was older, came to the clinic because of his indistinct speech. He was eleven years old; he had normal intelligence; he had a slight hearing loss in the left ear; and he had been slow in learning to talk. His first interview indicated that possibly he was a personality problem. He shrugged his shoulders and made no responses when asked a question. He would turn his head away from the examiner and look out of the corners of his eyes, as though surveying the dangers of the situation. His first reading of a simple story was entirely unintelligible. He apparently made no consonants whatsoever. Upon examination of individual words, he was found to say "egg" as "ed," "wagon" as "a," "letter" as "eder," and "watch" as "a." This child had been allowed to proceed in his class work along with the others with no speech help. After he became convinced that someone could help him speak like any normal boy, he worked diligently and in a few months he made unusual progress. He had excellent cooperation from his parents who brought him regularly to the clinic.

Still another child, who was allowed to drift until she became a junior in high school, came to the clinic with the speech substitutions of a child. She was found to have normal intelligence. Although she had poor discrimination of speech sounds, her hearing was practically normal. Her mother reported that she had never talked plainly. She spent three hours weekly in the clinic, in addition to two hours daily work at home. Overcoming her speech defect was the most important thing in her life since she was at an age when she desired favorable social responses. After diligent practice, she was able to talk as any normal person. However, poor speech for sixteen years is much more difficult to overcome than the speech defects of the five-year-old child with his less firmly established habits.

Two college students were having a most difficult task of overcoming some infantile speech habits. Until recently, one fellow was too shy to come to the clinic even to ask about his speech. The other fellow showed many emotional maladjustments. Both young men had suffered a feeling of speech inferiority since childhood. One of the young men said "Woo you wet me wight the wamp?" for "Will you let me light the lamp?" The substitution of *w* for *l* made his speech sound childish. The other fellow had a bad lisping *s*, which gave a sputtering *th* sound. Both of these young men were convinced that they should strive to attain normal speech suitable for men of their ages.

Causes of Sound Errors

Many of the substitutions of children are due to faulty training, too much isolation, overstimulation, defective models for imitation, and too much criticism by the parents. Many of the organic defects of the speech apparatus may be repaired if the child is taken to the surgeon or orthodonist early enough. The teeth may need to be straightened before the child can say some of his sounds. If the front teeth have not appeared yet, and the *s* is defective, the best plan usually is to wait for the teeth to appear. The *s* may take care of itself. If hearing loss is suspected, an audiometric check should be made to determine whether the child is hearing all of the different speech sounds accurately. The parents should also try to remove any unfavorable factors in the child's environment which may be impeding his progress.

Speech Therapy

After certain existing organic factors and psychological influences have been eliminated, actual speech re-education may take place. Auditory, visual, and kinesthetic methods are used in treating sound deviations. If the child makes several substitutions, the most simple sounds should be corrected first. The order of the sounds, according to least difficulty, are *p*, *b*, *m*, *t*, *d*, *n*, *th*, *f*, *v*, *s*, *z*, *k*, *g*, *l*, and *r*.

Parents may help their child to discriminate between sounds by playing games with him. For instance, a hissing sound is made: "s—s—s." The parent may say, "Did I hiss like a snake, 's—s—s,' or make a noise like the goose, 'th—th—th'?" Other sounds which may be included in the game of distinctions may be: "Did I 'f—f—f' like the cat or 'th—th—th—th' like the goose?" and "Did I 'r—r—r' like the angry dog or 'woo—woo—woo' like the wolf?"

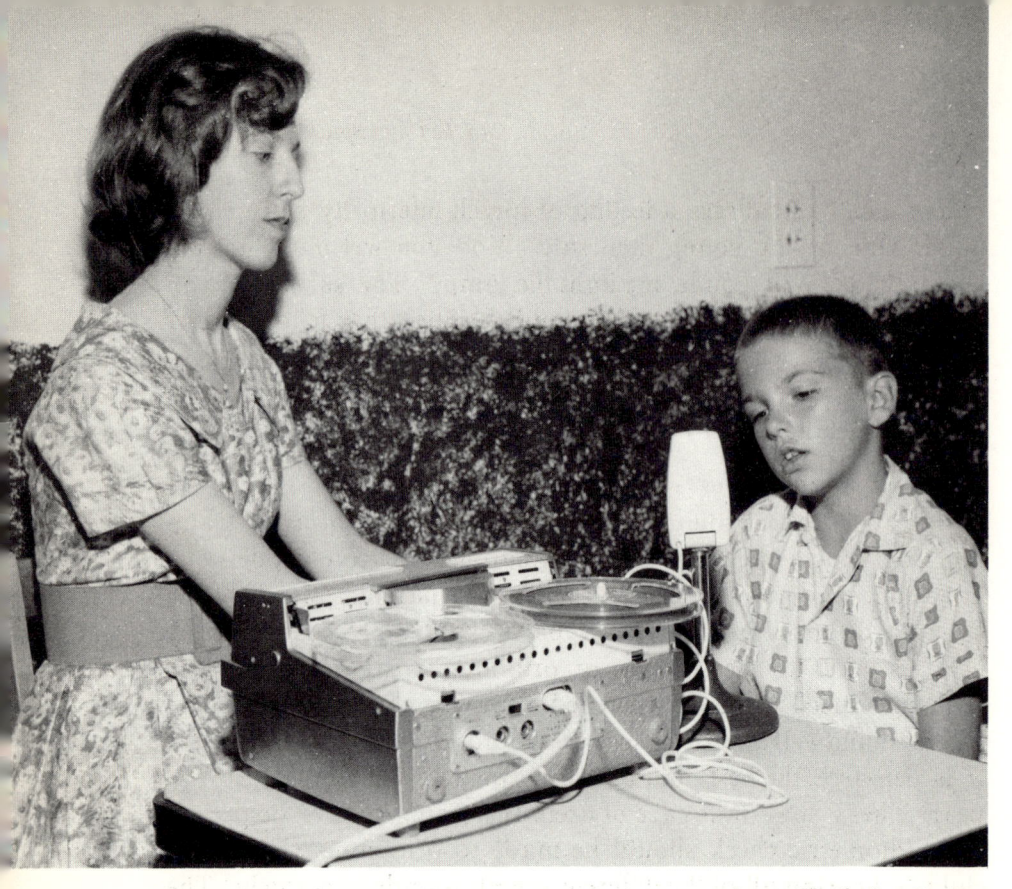

Courtesy The Ohio State University.

A child is recording speech on tape recorder. This procedure is used to measure improvement of speech before and after therapy and also helps the child to hear his own speech when the tape is replayed.

Picture books with animals will furnish stimulation for the various noises that are produced. Mother may say, "What does the cow say?" The right response brings "moo, moo" which helps the child to acquire a stronger *m* sound. With imagination, the parent may think of many possibilities to help the child to attain correct discriminations. Simple stories may be read with this type of suggestion to the child: "Listen carefully. Whenever you hear the sound like the snake makes, 's—s—s—s,' clap your hands." Children like to do this. Any sound which gives the child difficulty may be practiced in this way.

After the child can discriminate among the various sounds, the sound may be made in isolation. The actual teaching of a sound should be done by a speech pathologist if at all possible. Usual-

Can the Child Speak Plainly

ly, the pathologist will use what is called the stimulus-response method. The sound is made several times as the child listens. When the pathologist nods his head, the child is expected to respond once. This procedure is repeated. Some speech workers use the mirror as an aid. A small mirror is given to the child and the teacher says to him, "Now watch how I make the *s* sound and see if you can make it as I do." Both the teacher and child can sit in front of a large mirror as the stimulus-response method is used.

Each individual speech sound must be strengthened before attempting to combine the sound into a word. One cannot expect

Group Speech Therapy: Children are motivated to respond to pictures.

Courtesy The Ohio State University.

the child to say "cat" as soon as he has learned to say the *k* sound. Invariably the child will say "tat" as usual, if the teaching of the sound is "rushed." When attempting to combine the sound with the word, the helper may prolong the sound in this manner, "s—s—s" and then add the rest of the word "oup" rather suddenly, not allowing the "th" to slip in between the "s" and "oup," as in "s—th—oup." Gradually, the word may be said faster.

To make "corrected" sounds habitual, daily practice is desirable; however, a parent or teacher needs guidance in how, or whether to do anything, to help the child. Facilities for speech therapy in the local community should be ascertained. If none are available, a staff member of the nearest university speech and hearing clinic may assist.

If the child is already receiving treatment for his speech disorder, cooperation with the clinician is important. Experience and research have shown that children whose parents also receive instruction in speech problems improve much more rapidly than the children who depend only upon one or two lessons each week by a speech clinician.

Since the child imitates speech, parents need to improve their own articulation and manner of talking.

Discussion of the child's speech difficulty in his presence is taboo. The child should not be criticized for his incorrect speech. The child should be allowed to develop independence. He should do some things for himself. Too much attention to the child's needs may keep him infantile. Any progress in the direction of development of independence seems to be a step toward speech adequacy.

The parent or teacher can do much to help the speech-handicapped child without actually assuming the role of the speech clinician. For instance, the development of happy home and school situations will aid some children. Medical or physical attention may help to alleviate any factors which are causing or adding to the speech problems. Cooperating with professional personnel in the guidance of the child to improved speech production will be an important role for the teacher or parent. Patience is required. It takes a long time to change habits of speech. The younger the child, usually, the more rapidly can changes in speech production be effected.

Summary

In the early speech training of the young child, there must be auditory stimulation. The child must be aware of speech sounds before he is ready to imitate them.

The sounds which are most easily seen are usually learned first. The norms, as developed by Poole and Templin, are included in this chapter.

Neglect of articulatory deviations may lead to personality problems in the older child or the adult. Usually, the articulatory error is due to some functional or non-organic factor. Faulty learning or lack of attention to speech sounds may account for many of the problems.

The parent or teacher can do much to help the young child with speech problems involving sound deviations. If there is a pathologist available, there should be close cooperation always between the parent or teacher and the pathologist. If one is not available, guidance should be secured from the staff of the nearest university speech clinic. Sound stimulation exercises with no attempt at getting the child to repeat sounds is usually a harmless but helpful way of directing the child on the way to correct speech patterns.

Problems and Projects

1. Read and report on one reference which discusses articulatory problems.

2. Describe the speech of one child who has speech sound deviations.

3. Make a picture dictionary of sounds for a particular child to be used in teaching the correct use of the chosen words.

4. Make a set of diagnostic picture cards which can be used in identifying sound deviations. (See list of words for speech notebook and diagnostic cards in Appendix.)

5. Listen to the speech of a child (other than your own) with articulatory problems. Try to identify his specific sound errors.

References

Johnson, W., et al. *Speech Handicapped School Children.* New York: Harper, 1956. Chap. 3.

Jones, M.V. *Baby Talk.* Springfield, Illinois: Charles C. Thomas, 1960.

Scott, L.B. and J.J. Thompson. *Talking Time.* St. Louis: Webster Publishing, 1951.

Van Riper, C. *Speech Correction: Principles and Methods.* New York: Prentice-Hall, 1954. Chap. 7.

Warkomski, R.C. and R.B. Irwin. *Play and Say.* Pittsburgh: Stanwix House, 1961. (Activities for reinforcement of 12 speech sounds: S-CH-K-P-T-TH-F-G-R-SH-L-B.)

Films

Speech Training for the Handicapped Child (Chicago: National Society for Crippled Children and Adults, Inc., 2023 West Ogden Avenue). Shows the summer rehabilitation programs at four college and university centers in Illinois. Includes diagnostic procedures, speech therapy, and recreation.

Good Speech for Gary (New York: McGraw-Hill, Text-Film Department, 330 W. 42nd Street). This is a film from the University of Southern California giving particular attention to speech improvement in the classroom.

Recordings

Poetry Time, an album of three records: "Jigs and Jingles," "Talking Time," "What Shall We Do Today?" and "In the Country." Read by May Hill Arbuthnot. Chicago: Scott Foresman.

Say and Sing, two record albums: I. "The Snake Sound," "The Rooster Sound," II. "The Cross Kitty Sound," "The Bee Sound," III. "The Goose Sound," "The Singing Sound," IV. "The Coughing Sound," "The Train Sound." Jeri Productions, 3212 Glendale Boulevard, Los Angeles 39, California.

Sounds Around Us, three records: "Around the House," "Around the Farm," "Around the Town." Chicago: Scott, Foresman.

7

Children With Stuttering Symptoms

It is comforting to know that many children with stuttering symptoms will develop some degree of speech fluency as general maturation takes place. However, one is not always sure when a child needs special guidance to overcome his speech repetitions. As the child grows older, stuttering may become firmly established and difficult to eradicate. Therefore, it is of the utmost importance that parents and teachers do all they can to provide the essentials necessary for the child to develop "normal" speech.

Since stuttering interferes with the person's ability to communicate words, one may conclude that the defect occurs in the speech apparatus. However, upon examination of the stutterer's lips, teeth, tongue, and larynx, usually nothing can be found to contribute to the production of the words. The child may be able to say *b* at one time, but not at other times. This would indicate that the organic mechanism was not instrumental in causing the disturbance.

Several factors seem to be particularly characteristic of stutterers. For instance, more boys tend to stutter than do girls. Secondly, intelligence seems to have no particular relationship to this group of speech-defective children. As a whole, the stutterers show intelligence as normal as any group of normally speaking children. Moreover, stuttering, unlike other speech problems, has rather definite periods for its onset. Speech hesitations or blockings may begin when the child starts to talk, when he starts to school, or when he begins the period of adolescence. At these particular times, various emotional adjustments are being made. Sometimes, a particularly nervous or sensitive child cannot make the social adaptations adequately, and the result may be stuttering.

When is the child a stutterer? Does he block (complete inability to say a word)? Does he repeat the beginning of a word, as "c—c—c—cat" before he can say all of the word? Does he talk too fast, or in jerky rhythm? All of these symptoms may be evidenced as the child learns to talk since the nervous speech mechanism matures slowly. However, if many hesitations or repetitions occur with accompanying facial grimaces, the child needs the sympathetic and understanding cooperation of his parents, teachers, and friends.

A mother may ask, "Why does my child stutter when my friend's little girl does not?" That is a question that many speech specialists have been trying to answer for years. Numerous researches have been made to ascertain the real causes for stuttering, but no outstanding agreement has been reached by speech authorities. Among the various reasons given for the onset of the stuttering symptoms are brain damage, diseases, inferiority complex, severe shocks, inability to adjust to a group, imitation, heredity, and slips of the tongue. Some believe that the boys are more likely to stutter than the girls, since they are expected to behave like "little gentlemen" and to learn how to be the future leaders of the nation. Members of society usually expect as much of a five-year-old boy as of a five-year-old girl. Since girls mature physically more quickly than boys do, boys are often subjected to undue pressures.

Some believe that severe frights and shocks will start hesitant speech. One small girl began stuttering shortly after the violent California earthquake. Another child developed slow, faltering speech when severely frightened by a burning rag, accidently caught in her hair. However, this shock of the burning rag followed a severe seige of whooping cough, which undoubtedly weakened the child's nervous constitution. Probably, no one factor is responsible for the onset of nervous speech. The one hard fall, an earthquake, whooping cough, measles, or a bad home environment may not be individually responsible for the onset of nervous speech. But, if the child had measles, *plus* a hard fall, *plus* a sudden shock, *plus* quarrelsome parents, he may stutter— "The last straw breaks the camel's back."

For centuries, many attempts have been made to cure stuttering. At one time, even a piece of the tongue was clipped off, in the hope that speech could be freed. Unusual appliances, also, were often attached to the tongue to aid the speaker. The much-quoted Demosthenes tried to free his speech by talking with pebbles in his mouth. At the present time, many methods are advocated for the stutterer to use. Some therapies seem to be more effective and lasting than others. No one set of rules will apply to every person. Talking slowly may help one and not another. In general, each stutterer must develop a proper attitude toward his difficulty; he must develop a "bag of tricks" that he may carry with him for any speech emergency.

The treatment of the young stutterer is different from that of the stuttering adult. In most cases, the child is not yet conscious of his speech deficiency. Consequently, it is important to "treat" the parent and his teacher, so that the child may not be allowed to develop any undue anxiety about his condition. Certain procedures must be followed, and certain procedures must be avoided if the child is to conquer his stumbling speech before deep-seated personality maladjustments take place.

Suggestions for helping the child to overcome his stuttering may be grouped under four headings: physical, psychological, sociological, and re-educational. The approach, also, should be made in much this same order.

Physical

To help the child to achieve physical health, all infections must be removed. Such conditions often initiate and produce extreme nervousness which of course is conducive to stuttering. In the maintenance of good health, a well-balanced diet, adequate rest, and exercise must be instituted. Regular periods for relaxation and rest should be provided during the day. A short rest after the noon and evening meals is helpful.

In addition to the removal of all physical infections, any physical abnormality which may affect the child's speech should be treated surgically if at all possible. Usually, however, the child who stutters has no organic disability. Parents and teachers should cooperate in every way with health officials in order that the child develops good health, which is the first step toward speech rehabilitation.

Psychological

Proper mental attitudes should be developed. All speech situations must be faced with courage. Obedience, perseverance, concentration, deliberation, organization, and calmness are characteristics favorable for the stutterer to cultivate. He should assume the attitude, "I will never hurry again. I have lots of time to talk."

All anxiety and fear in regard to speaking must be avoided. If the child once notices that his speech is inadequate, or that he is causing unpleasant reactions among his friends, he will begin to fear talking. Fear will gradually make stuttering worse and difficult to handle. If the child is already much distressed over his inability to speak fluently, he should be convinced that everyone stutters some, now and then. If someone tells the child that he stutters, he may say, "Sure I stutter! Everyone does!"

The child who stutters should never be forced to compete with others in school work or games. Pressure situations such as produced through the use of flash cards and speed drills will increase the tension of the stutterer. The child may be brilliant, but his emotional make-up will not allow him to compete in scholastic or athletic tension-producing situations without detriment to his speech fluency.

No emotional responses should be given by the parent or teacher to the child who has difficulty in speaking. Stuttering must be ignored. After a severe stuttering spasm, his attention should be diverted to pleasant activities, so that his thoughts will not dwell on his speech failure.

The child's confidence must be developed. Whenever possible, he should be praised. Development of a new skill will frequently add to the child's feeling of importance. It is essential that each child feel that he does something very well.

If the child has passed from the stage of stuttering in which he is unaware of his difficulty to the stage in which he is conscious of his stuttering, he should be convinced that his speech organs are probably perfectly normal and that he can talk as well as anyone else. Reading in unison, singing, or talking to animals often reveal to the stutterer that he is capable of fairly fluent speech.

Sociological

The home, school, and community environments may contribute to the child's feelings of inferiority and insecurity, which often intensify the stuttering. The various environments should be closely examined to determine what undesirable elements exist and need to be eliminated.

The home must be free from tension-producing situations. Conflicts between parents often produce an atmosphere that is disturbing to the child. It is not enough to conceal disturbances; they must be removed. Even though problems are not discussed in the presence of the child, he is likely to sense that the parents are worried.

Parents need to be examples of calm living. If they behave calmly and use slow speech, the child may tend to slow down. Parents should also check themselves for any unfavorable habits which may be contributing to the child's feeling of insecurity. In every way possible, the child's home should be filled with calm activity, regular routine, and a congenial atmosphere.

The satisfactory personal adjustment of the child who stutters is dependent in a large measure upon his classroom teacher who should be in good physical, mental, and emotional health. The teacher may cooperate in removing all tension-producing stimuli from the child's environment. Her manner and speech should be calm. The teacher as well as the parent may control the attitude of the children in the schoolroom and the neighborhood by treating the child who stutters as a "normal" person, and as one who is not inferior or in need of sympathy. The children in the classroom should be asked to cooperate in overlooking the young child's unsuccessful attempts to speak. It might be well for the teacher to point out that almost everyone has some type of difficulty such as talking too fast, reading too slowly, not paying attention in class, wearing glasses or hearing aids, or using

Courtesy Better Homes and Gardens *and Ohio University.*

After the child names the picture, the speech clinician says the word one or two times in order to provide a correct auditory pattern for the child to imitate.

crutches. Children should learn to continue work and play without noticing the unfortunate speaker.

Re-educational

The physical condition has been checked and attempts have been made to improve the general health; the environment has been examined and all unfavorable factors have been removed or corrected; the right mental attitude has been established toward the speech inadequacy. The child is now ready to do some direct speech work.

The parent or teacher should provide as many ideal speaking situations for the child who stutters as possible. He must never be forced or encouraged to talk when he is tired or excited.

Use of the telephone, taking part in conversations, dramatics, oral recitations and public speaking, going shopping, and making introductions are activities which help the child to think less of himself and of his speaking. Each speech activity mastered will tend to give the speaker more confidence. One should begin with the easier speaking situations first, and then proceed to the more difficult assignments as the success warrants.

During the evening story hour, the parent may be able to help the child to talk easily without attracting particular attention to his difficulty. For instance, he may be taught how to relax by playing games with him. He may pretend to be a scarecrow. The rain makes his head droop over and then the sun comes, making his head come up again and back. Or the child may be a "Raggedy Ann." As relaxation games are played, speech may gradually be added to accompany the actions. It is usually very easy for the stutterer to talk slowly when relaxed.

After an introduction to relaxation, rhymes may be read in slow tempo, pausing between short phrases for breath. The child may repeat the sentences after the teacher or parent in the same way. If he can think of sighing as he talks, he will have less difficulty. All first words of sentences should be attacked easily, as these are the words that the children usually fear.

In the schoolroom, the child should be asked to recite only when he volunteers; however, the teacher should encourage him to talk in class. She should gain his point of view in regard to how and when he wishes to recite. Extra written work may be given to the child who stutters if he is to be excused from oral recitation. This requirement would be conducive to thorough preparation of each lesson. In mathematics, for example, the child with the speech difficulty may place the problem on the board. Another child may explain the problem. In this way, the speech-handicapped child has an opportunity to participate actively in the class recitation.

Whenever possible, the class should read selections in unison.

The child who stutters should be encouraged to read also. He will find that he has very little difficulty in reading with others. Moreover, taking parts in dramatizations will be easy, since the stutterer acts the part of someone who does not stutter, and for the time that he is acting the part of someone else, he is likely to stutter with less frequency. Meeting successful speaking attempts, such as found in acting or choral reading, will help to build the child's self-confidence tending to eliminate his fear of talking. He will also become convinced that he is capable of "normal" fluency.

Whenever the child does have difficulty in speaking, he should be allowed to take as much time as he needs. He should never be told to stop and start over again, to swallow, to talk faster, or to swing his arms. In fact, nothing should be said or done that would in any way call attention to his non-fluent speech.

Summary

Many reasons have been given for the causation of stuttering. No one knows for certain the exact cause. It appears that anything which tends to make the child grow anxious about the speech process may contribute to stuttering. One authority has indicated that labeling the slow beginnings of speech as "stuttering" by parents may initiate what is considered to be stuttering.

Children with stuttering symptoms vary considerably in regard to degree and conditions of stuttering. Some stutter more in the evening than in the morning; others will stutter more with fathers than with mothers; some will stutter more at home than at school. All stutterers appear to be able to read or sing together with little difficulty in speech.

The treatment program involves attention to four areas: physical, psychological, sociological, and re-educational. With sympathetic understanding and cooperation, the parents and teachers may do much in the home and school toward helping the child who stutters to overcome his handicap before any personality maladjustments occur. Whenever possible, the "stuttering" child and his parents should be guided by a competent speech pathologist.

Problems and Projects

1. Report a case history of a child who stutters. Point out the factors which may contribute to the problem.
2. Read Johnson's chapter on "The Clinical Point of View" *(Speech Handicapped School Children)*. Give your reactions.
3. Keep a daily diary for one week of the situations in which your child stutters. State how you reacted each time.
4. In what way can parents help children who stutter?
5. Observe at least one group session for the treatment of stutterers. Report your observations.
6. How can classroom teachers assist the stuttering child?

References

Belgum, D. "Stuttering." *Hygeia,* 22:345—347, 1944.

Johnson, W. *Stuttering and What You Can Do About It.* Minneapolis: University of Minnesota Press, 1961.

Johnson, W., et al. "The Clinical Point of View in Education." "Stuttering." "An Open Letter to the Mother of a Stuttering Child." *Speech Handicapped School Children.* New York: Harper, 1956, Chap. 2, Chap. 5, pp. 558—567.

Van Riper, C. *Stuttering.* Ed. W. Johnson. Chicago: National Society for Crippled Children and Adults, 1948. (Pamphlet prepared for the American Speech and Hearing Association.)

Films

Stuttering, From the Horse's Mouth (State University of Iowa Film Library), 33 minutes.

Search: Stuttering (State University of Iowa Film Library), 27 minutes.

8
Children With Cerebral Palsy

Esther was only one out of nearly 200,000 children in the United States suffering from cerebral palsy. Yet to her mother, the problems associated with the disorder were relatively unknown and certainly largely misunderstood by the average person. Because little attention was given to the child with cerebral palsy until the last few years, Esther reached the age of sixteen with inadequate treatment although thousands of dollars had been spent by her well-to-do parents in trying to secure professional help. Growing discouraged, Esther grew dependent upon her mother who sacrificed her own personal life to satisfy her daughter's demands.

"What shall I do with her?" the mother would anxiously ask each doctor as she searched frantically for the answers to her problem. Today, many years later, Esther's mother could probably have found professional guidance early enough to have avoided some of the major psychological problems from developing.

What is the condition known as cerebral palsy? According to Dr. Phelps, "Cerebral palsy is a disability of the nerves and muscles caused by damage to certain centers of the brain that govern muscular control." Due to the injury of certain tissues of the brain, the muscles of the body are without proper control. As a result, the child is not able to coordinate his movements as well as the normal child. His eyes are often uncontrollable. This condition may handicap his progress in reading. His feet may not be so easily controlled, and he is forced to "shamble along."

Depending upon the part of the brain injured, certain parts of the body may be affected. Only one side of the body may be paralyzed, or both sides, or only the hands, or only the legs.

Since it is difficult to locate all of the children afflicted with cerebral palsy because many have been hidden in "the farthest corner" away from neighbors and friends, no definite number can be given. It has been estimated that three or four children out of every one thousand school children are afflicted by cerebral palsy.

The speech of the child with cerebral palsy cannot be understood adequately without understanding the nature of cerebral palsy. It is the purpose of this chapter to discuss briefly these topics: incidence, types, causes, diagnosis, and therapy.

Incidence

There are seven children born with cerebral palsy each year for every 100,000 of the general population. Of these seven, one will die before the age of six, two will be feebleminded, and four will be educable. Of the children with cerebral palsy, 75 per cent have speech problems. It is estimated that 50 to 75 per cent of these children with speech deviations can benefit by speech training.

Children with cerebral palsy often have multiple problems. It has already been indicated that one of the problems may be speech and another one may be mental deficiency. Because of the physical impairment, reading and writing problems may occur. About 50 per cent of the children have visual defects; about 65 per cent are left handed.

Types

The major types of cerebral palsy of most interest to the speech clinician are the following: (1) athetoid, (2) spastic, and (3) ataxic.

Athetoid. The athetoid group makes up about 40 to 45 per cent of the whole group of cerebral palsied persons. The athetoids are divided into the "tension athetoids" and the "non-tension athetoids." The athetoid person appears to be unable to stop his involuntary movements of muscles. The "tension athetoid" develops habitual tension in his attempt to resist some of his involuntary movements; whereas, the "non-tension" type makes little attempt to stop his movements.

Spastic. The spastic group composes about 40 per cent of the whole group. Three kinds of muscle conditions may exist in the spastic person: (1) muscles may be flaccid, (2) muscles may be normal, and (3) muscles may be "spastic." "Spastic" means a hypertonicity or extreme tension which varies from a slight amount to extreme rigidity.

Ataxic. The ataxic group makes up about 20 per cent of the total group. Incoordination, lack of balance, and exaggerated motions may characterize the ataxic person.

Causes

The authorities agree that cerebral palsy is caused by a defect in the brain. The main question is: what caused the brain defect? Phelps indicates that the majority of the brain injuries come from developmental difficulties or from injury at the time of birth.

Diagnosis

A team of professional "experts" is needed for making adequate diagnosis of all the needs of the cerebral palsied individual. Not only should this team determine the needs, but it should also recommend proper therapy after due consideration and unified consultation have taken place. The probable prognosis may have to wait for a trial period of therapy since proper evaluation of the person's ability to progress in therapy may be affected by his physical handicap.

The following "experts" should be a part of the team which operates in the best interests of the child: (1) the neurologist who determines the *amount, area,* and *type* of palsy; (2) the psychologist who estimates the intellectual ability and social adjustment; (3) the pediatrician who gives the physical examination; (4) the speech pathologist who gives special speech and hearing tests; (5) the orthopedist who evaluates needs for braces or surgery; and (6) the physical therapist who assists the neurologist and orthopedist in predicting what the child may be able to do. Other members of the team will be described in the discussion on therapy.

Therapy

Mary Jane was getting excellent physical therapy, but her parents were still concerned. She did not talk as well as a six-year-old child should. A visit to a speech clinician revealed that Mary Jane did need speech therapy. Not only did Mary Jane need the services of a speech clinician, but she needed treatment from all members of the team of "experts."

The complete program of rehabilitation requires the coordination of the services of the neurologist, the psychologist, the pediatrician, the speech pathologist, the orthopedist, the physical therapist, the occupational therapist, and the professional educator. The parent is a very important part of the program also.

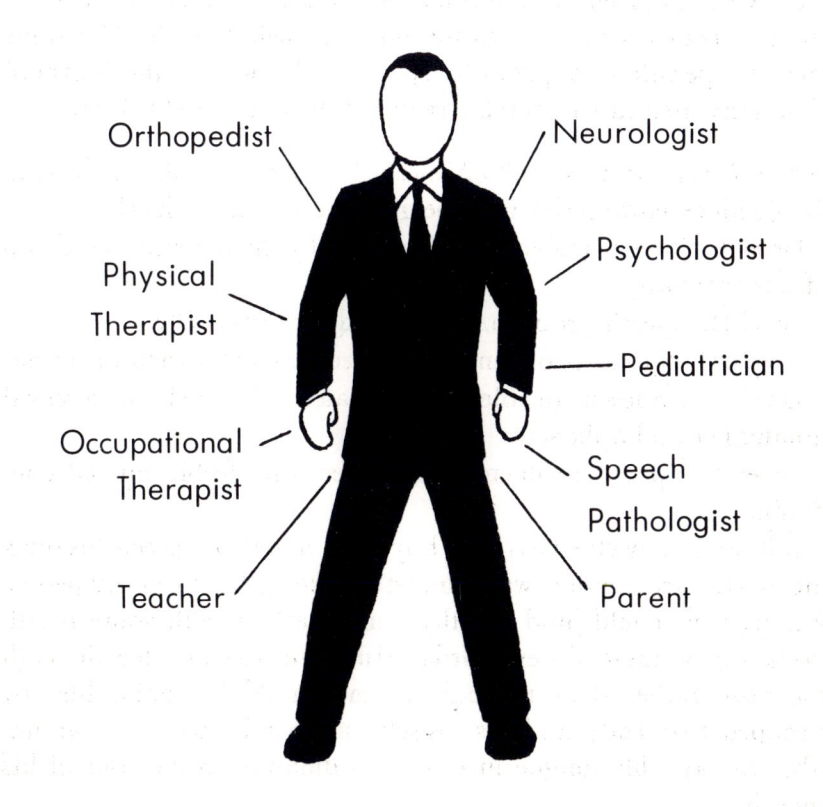

Figure 4. The Team of "Experts" Coordinating the Services for the Cerebral Palsied Child

Speech Rehabilitation

Normality is not the aim of speech treatment for the cerebral palsied child. The goal is to work for the best speech that the damaged mechanisms are capable of producing. "Correction" implies that speech can be made perfect and that is not usually possible.

Speech is an "overlaid function." There is no part of the anatomy which was intended primarily for speech. The teeth, tongue, and jaws are for eating; the lungs are for breathing; and the throat is for swallowing. For the person with some muscular involvement in any one of these areas, speech may become difficult. However, children and adults with cerebral palsy may have speech problems not due to the physical defect at all. The same factors operating to produce speech difficulties in the "normal" child may also cause speech irregularities in the cerebral child.

Five Levels of Speech Problems. The speech problems of children with cerebral palsy may be grouped into these levels:

Level I. Speech problems not caused by the physical handicap of cerebral palsy.

Level II. Speech problems associated with spasticity.

Level III. Speech problems associated with athetosis and ataxia.

Level IV. Speech problems associated with lack of cerebral dominance and aphasias.

Level V. Speech problems associated with feeble-minded condition.

Bill was a twelve-year-old boy with a severe speech involvement. His articulation was almost unintelligible to many people although he could hold lengthy conversations with some repetitions and writing of key words. Much air was directed through the nose rather than through the mouth. As he spoke, his jaw dropped frequently and his muscles almost "locked." He was unable to raise his tongue in easy coordination to the roof of his mouth.

The speech clinicians tried a variety of techniques with Bill. The child's interest in speech was high, but he did not improve much. Attempts were made to control the wrinkling of his nose as the boy talked. Relaxation was tried; blowing exercises to direct the air through the mouth instead of the nose were tried; and a direct attempt at retraining in articulation was made. At best, progress in speech rehabilitation for the cerebral palsied child is slow. Much depends upon the intelligence, damage, motivation, and understanding of the parents.

Specific speech therapy is provided by a speech clinician whenever possible and as often as facilities allow. In the public schools, twice a week may be as frequent as the child can be seen by the speech clinician who must visit several schools. In the large cities, the orthopedic school may have speech services on a daily basis. Any speech therapy needs to be supplemented by help from all members of the team and also from the parents at home.

Speech techniques may be observed by visiting a speech clinician who works with cerebral palsied children. Basic approaches, as well as specific techniques, will vary considerably from clinician to clinician. The types of therapy used will depend a great deal upon the needs and abilities of each child.

Relaxation is often used as a basis for accurate speech production. The athetoid child can usually do a better job of talking if his hands are kept busy with activities of some kind. The spastic child will profit from definite repetitive practice of speech exercises, but care should be taken to avoid overworking the child.

In all speech work, the speech clinician needs to work closely with all of the other therapists in the center or those associated with the child in order that the speech practice becomes an hourly activity rather than a once- or twice-a-week affair.

Community and National Resources

Much interest has developed locally and nationally in the rehabilitation of the cerebral palsied person. Private agencies often establish clinics for the physically handicapped child with staff and consultants to provide adequate treatment in all areas needed by the child.

The city superintendent of schools will usually be able to tell the parents about the opportunities for diagnosis and therapy in the local community. Other resources include the nearest university speech and hearing clinic or the State Division of Special Education.

Summary

Parents are often resentful or feel guilty when a cerebral palsied child is born. One of the most difficult tasks for the parent is to accept this crippled child with an attitude of constructive planning.

Over 200,000 children in the United States have the cerebral palsied condition. Probably 75 per cent of them have speech problems. The major types of cerebral palsy are athetoid, spastic, and ataxic.

A team of "experts" is needed in the diagnosis and rehabilitation of the cerebral palsied child. Speech re-education must be attempted in terms of the damaged structures, the intelligence of the child, his motivation, and the intelligent cooperation of his parents.

Resources are now available for the parent who seeks help for his handicapped child.

Problems and Projects

1. Visit the nearest cerebral palsy center for children and observe all types of therapy given to the children. Explain in your report on the observation how speech therapy is coordinated with physical or occupational activities.

2. Read and report on an article or book about cerebral palsy.

3. Write or tell about a child who has cerebral palsy and also has speech problems.

4. What facilities are available in your community for cerebral palsied children?

5. What special problems may parents of cerebral palsied children have? Do all of these problems differ from those of parents of children with other types of speech problems? Explain.

References

Carlson, E.R. *Born That Way.* New York: John Day, 1941.

Gratke, J.M. "Speech Problems of the Cerebral Palsied." *Journal of Speech Disorders,* XII (1947), 129–134.

Huber, M. "Letter to the Parents of the Cerebral Palsied Child."

Journal of Speech and Hearing Disorders, XV (1950), 154—158.

Levinson, H.J. "A Parent Training Program for a Cerebral Palsy Unit." *Journal of Speech and Hearing Disorders,* XIX (1954), 253—257.

Longerich, M.C. "Speech for the Cerebral Palsied Pre-School Child." Los Angeles: College of Medical Evangelists, School of Medicine. (Leaflet of suggestions to parents.)

McKibben, S. "The Spastic Situation." *Journal of Speech Disorders,* VIII (1943), 147—153.

Phelps, W.M. and T.A. Turner. *The Farthest Corner.* Elyria, Ohio: National Society for Crippled Children and Adults.

Perlstein, M.A. and M. Shere. "Speech Therapy for Children With Cerebral Palsy." *American Journal of Diseases of Children,* LXXII (1946), 389—398.

Rutherford, B.R. *Give Them a Chance to Talk.* Minneapolis: Burgess Publishing, 1950.

Westlake, H. "A System for Developing Speech With Cerebral Palsied Children." *The Crippled Child,* (June, August, October, December, 1951).

Films

Search: Cerebral Palsy (National Association of American Business Clubs in cooperation with National Society for Crippled Children and Adults, 2023 West Ogden Avenue, Chicago 12, Illinois), 26 minutes. The purpose of the film is to help people to understand the problems faced by cerebral palsied persons.

A Place in the Sun (Junior League of San Francisco, Mark Hopkins Hotel, San Francisco 8, California), 23 minutes. Illustrates the treatment of a cerebral palsied child at the California State School for Cerebral Palsied Children at Redwood City, California.

Out of the Shadows (Los Angeles: USC Audio-Visual Services, 3518 University Avenue). A twenty-minute film shows how one institution trained children with cerebral palsy.

9
Children With Cleft-Palate Speech

Richard was born with a cleft of the hard and soft palates. He also had a bilateral cleft of the lip. His parents were shocked to discover that their first-born child was disfigured. The term "cleft palate" was an unknown term to them. They did not know that present-day treatment could offer much to alleviate the condition. Surgery plus speech therapy helped Richard to attain fairly adequate speech.

Types

A cleft palate may or may not be accompanied by a cleft lip. Figures 5 and 6 will indicate two types of cleft palates and three cleft-lip conditions.

TABLE II Sex Distribution According to Types of Cleft Palates[1]

Type	Males	Females
Cleft Lip	53	35
Cleft Lip and Cleft Palate	168	77
Cleft Palate	81	86

1. M.C. Oldfield, "Modern Trends in Harelip and Cleft-Palate Surgery," *The British Journal of Surgery*, XXXVII (1950), 179–192.

Children With Cleft-Palate Speech

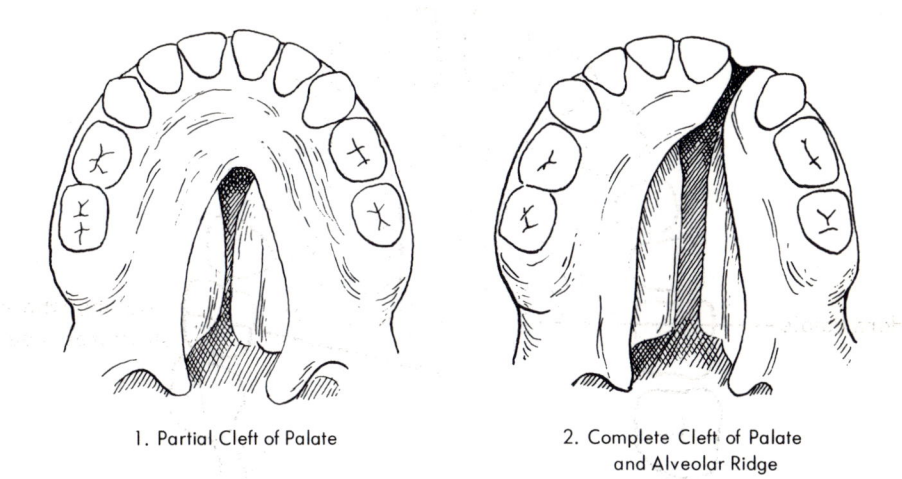

1. Partial Cleft of Palate

2. Complete Cleft of Palate and Alveolar Ridge

Figure 5. Two Types of Cleft Palate

Among 1000 cases, Fogh-Anderson[2] found that 25 per cent of the cases had cleft lip only, 50 per cent had both cleft of lip and hard and soft palates, and 25 per cent had cleft of soft palate only.

Sex differences occur in the types of cleft palates. Table II will illustrate the variations occurring between boys and girls. As in other types of handicaps, it appears that the boys are more likely to have cleft-palate disorders than girls.

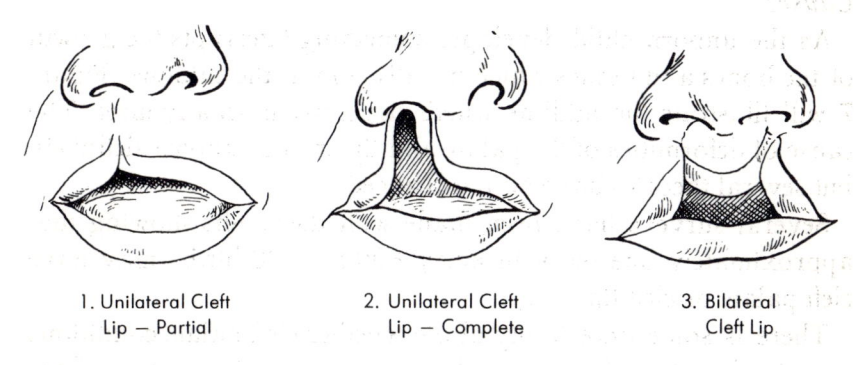

1. Unilateral Cleft Lip — Partial

2. Unilateral Cleft Lip — Complete

3. Bilateral Cleft Lip

Figure 6. Three Types of Cleft Lip

2. P. Fogh-Anderson, *Inheritance of Harelip and Cleft Palate* (Copenhagen: Nyt Nordish Forlag. Arnold Busch, 1942), p. 33.

77

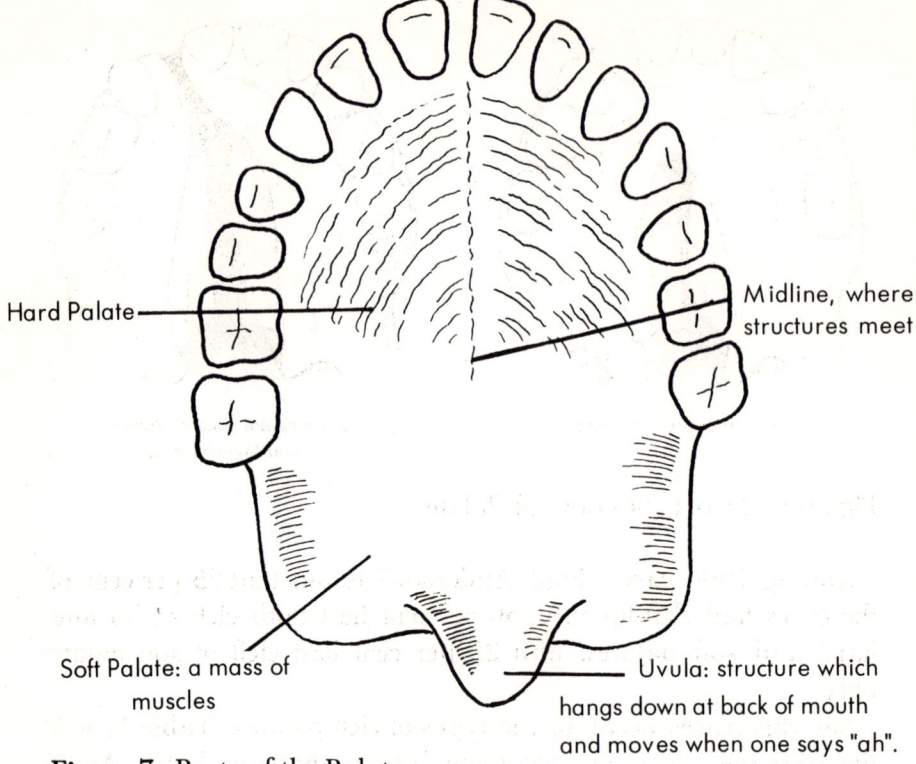

Figure 7. Parts of the Palate

Labels: Hard Palate; Midline, where structures meet; Soft Palate: a mass of muscles; Uvula: structure which hangs down at back of mouth and moves when one says "ah".

Causes

As the unborn child develops, something interrupts the growth of the bones and tissues which usually join in the midline. Figure 7 will illustrate the midline where structures normally meet. The cause of deformities of the palate and lip are not known definitely but several theories have been advanced.

Several surveys have been made with the results showing that approximately one baby in every 800 to 1000 births may have cleft palate or cleft lip.

There is some uncertainty about whether cleft-palate conditions "run in families." In one study of 42 cases, 38 per cent of the children with palatal abnormalities came from families with histories of cleft palate. Roughly, 80 per cent of babies with cleft palate are born into families with no known history of the defect,

Children With Cleft-Palate Speech

and in 20 per cent there has been a history of cleft palates some place in the family background.

What to Do?

Many problems confront the parents of a child born with a defective palate or/and lip. In order to provide the best services for the child, the combined counseling and treatments by several professional specialities are needed. In Figure 8 the parent may visualize the many aspects of the rehabilitation of the child born with a cleft palate.

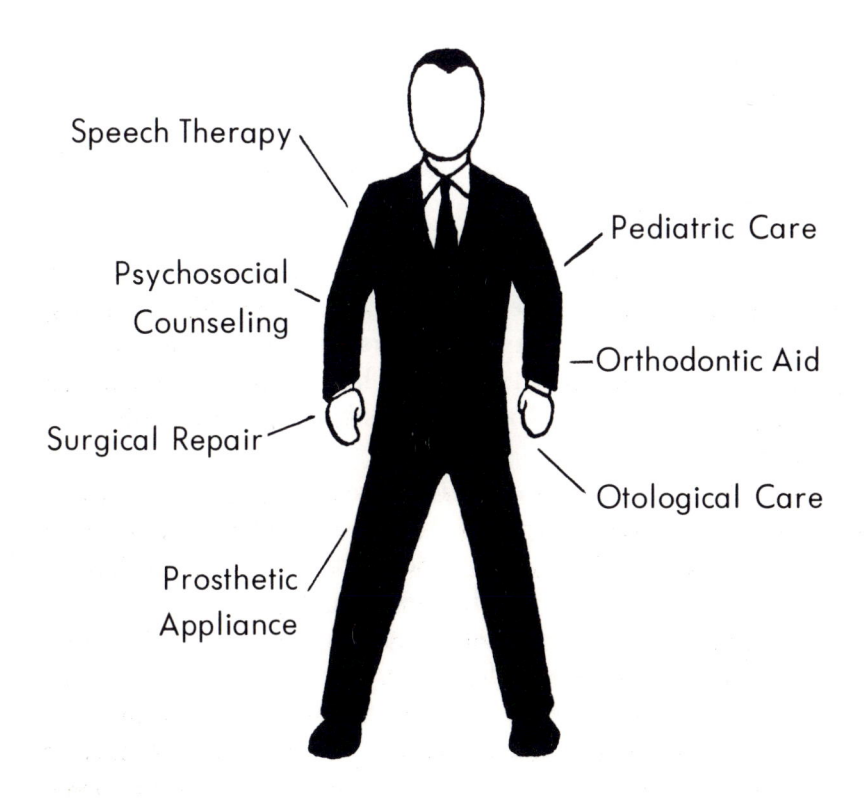

Figure 8. Various Types of Treatment Usually Needed by a a Child Born With a Cleft Palate

79

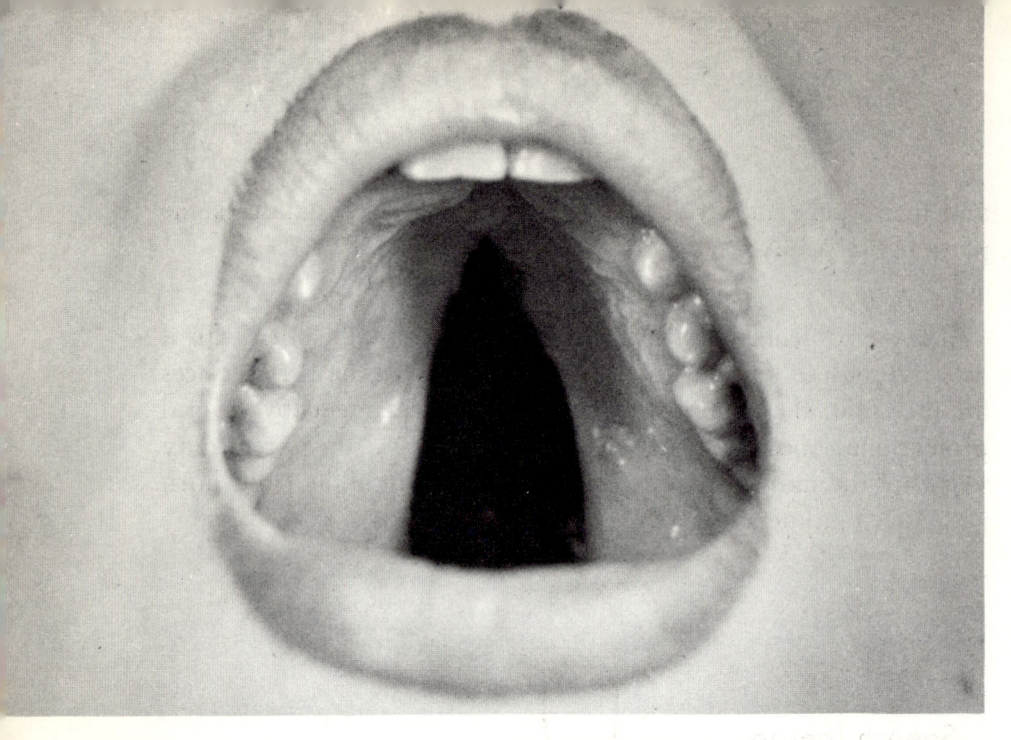

Courtesy Howard E. Kessler, D.D.S., Dentofacial Speech Consultant to the Cleveland Public Schools.

Unrepaired cleft palate.

In some communities, a team of "experts" meets to examine and discuss the course of treatment for the cleft-palate child. Questions, such as the following, may be discussed: Should we operate? Does he need further operation? Would he profit by an appliance? Is he ready for speech? How about his hearing? Will orthodontia help?

Speech Training. Speech training is recommended and provided as early as possible and advisable. The child needs to start speech lessons in order to avoid developing poor speech habits. For the young preschool child, speech training may be given by the parent under the guidance of the speech pathologist. For other young children, speech stimulation may be provided in the clinic.

The improvement of voice quality and the accurate production of sounds are the two main goals of therapy. Several factors determine the degree of success which may be expected from speech therapy: (1) intelligence, (2) hearing, (3) emotional stability, (4) muscular coordination, (5) "speech readiness," (6) motivation, (7) existing habits of breath direction and articulation, (8) age of child when operation was done, (9) age of child when speech

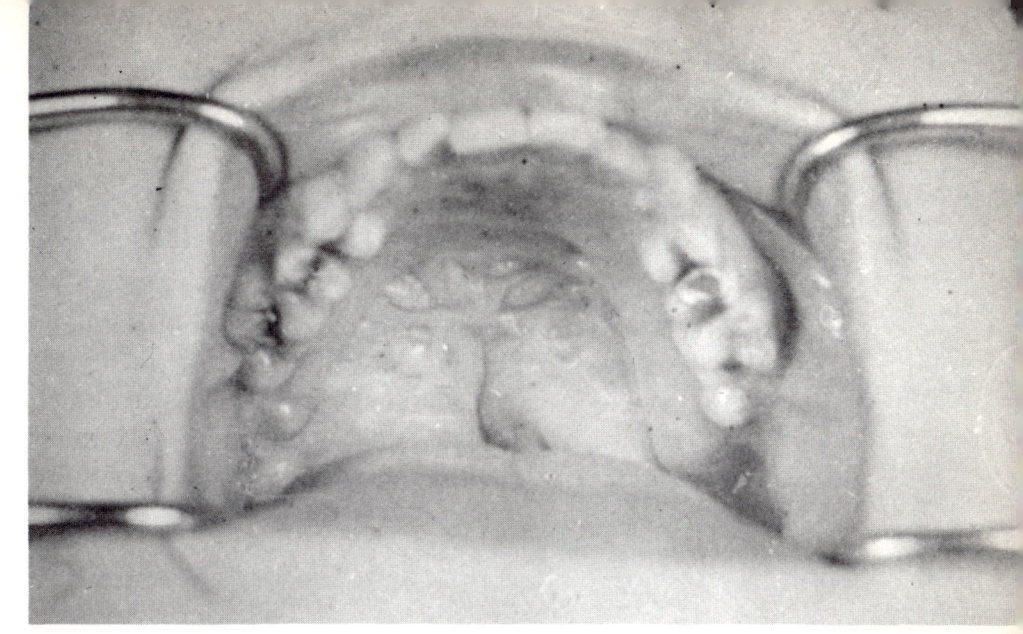

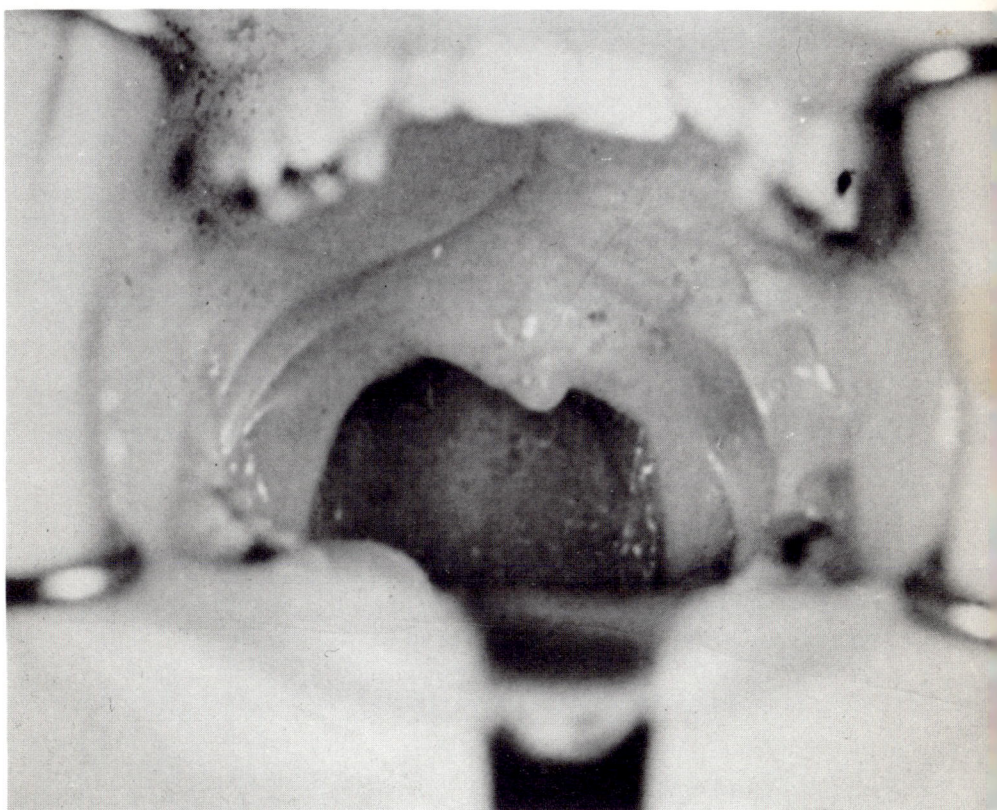

Courtesy Howard E. Kessler, D.D.S., Dentofacial Speech Consultant to the Cleveland Public Schools.

Repaired cleft palate.

therapy is begun, and (10) attitude of child and parent toward problems.

Steps in Speech Therapy. Usually the procedures used in the treatment of cleft-palate speech (except for preschool children) include these steps: (1) Strengthening the muscles of the soft palate, (2) Directing the air and sound through the "wide open" mouth, (3) Recognizing nasal voice quality and inaccurate sound production through eartraining, (4) Producing the pleasing voice

A child learns to direct breath through the mouth instead of the nose.

Courtesy Cleveland Public Schools.

quality in "ah" or correct sound in isolation, (5) Using the non-nasal quality or correct sound in a short word, (6) Transferring correct speech patterns to sentences, and finally (7) Using speech as adequately as possible in conversational speech. Socialization is an important factor in the treatment program. Many of the speech lessons are social.

In addition to speech therapy, the child will need understanding and help from his teachers, parents, and others. As much as possible, the child should be treated as a "normal" child. If the parents are not anxious and alarmed about the child's condition, the child will be less likely to develop unfavorable personality reactions. Specifically, the parent (1) Admits calmly and unemotionally that his child was born with a cleft palate, (2) Avoids feeling sorry for the child, (3) Helps the child to accept his problems realistically, (4) Treats him as any other child, (5) Encourages the child to speak, and (6) Finds services for the child.

Community Resources

The nearest university speech and hearing clinic will have staff members who can usually advise parents of cleft-palate children where diagnostic and therapeutic services may be obtained. If financial support is needed to help with surgical or speech rehabilitation, the State Division of Crippled Children will often assist.

Other state and community resources may include: state department of education, medical and nursing associations, public-health nurses, and private clinics.

Summary

Approximately one baby in every 800 to 1000 births may have cleft palate or cleft lip. Various types and combinations of clefts are illustrated in this chapter. The cleft lip in combination with the cleft palate is the most frequent, particularly among boys.

A team of specialists is desirable for the diagnosis and treatment of the child born with clefts of the palate and lip. Speech therapy is begun as early as possible so as to avoid poor habits in speech.

The parent should seek guidance from specialists for their child with cleft palate. Close and understanding cooperation of all persons concerned with the welfare of the child is desired.

Problems and Projects

1. Describe the speech of the child with a cleft palate.
2. Write an observation report on speech therapy for cleft-palate children.
3. Attend a clinic for cleft-palate children where the team approach is used. Write your observations.
4. Write the life story of some child or person with cleft palate.
5. Describe the various types of cleft-palate and cleft-lip conditions.

References

Backus, O.L., J.N. Clancy, L.D. Henry, and J. Kemper. *The Child With a Cleft Palate.* Pamphlet. Ann Arbor: University of Michigan Press, 1949.

Backus, O.L. "Children With Cleft Palate and Cleft Lip." *Speech Problems of Children.* Ed. W. Johnson. New York: Grune and Stratton, 1950.

Gardner, W.H., ed. "A Child Has a Cleft Palate." Pamphlet. Cleveland: Cleveland Junior Chamber of Commerce, 1949.

McDonald, E.T. *Bright Promise: For Your Child With Cleft Lip and Palate.* Parent Series No. 6. Chicago: National Society for Crippled Children and Adults, 1959.

Wells, C.G. and G.M. Phair. "Speech Training for Cleft Palate Children: A Teacher-Parent Guide." Madison, Wisconsin: Department of Public Instruction, 1957.

Films

The Wisconsin Cleft Palate Story (The Wisconsin State Department of Education, Bureau of Visual Instruction, University of Wisconsin Extension Division, 1328 W. Johnson Street, Madison).

Cleft Palate Speech in the Child (University of Michigan Film Library, Ann Arbor), 30 minutes.

Rehabilitation of Patients With Clefts of Lip and Palate (State University of Iowa Film Library, Iowa City), 36 minutes.

Part Three

Related Problems

10

Is He Hard of Hearing?

Tommy was five years old when his mother became concerned about his hearing. Fortunately, the University Speech and Hearing Center was located nearby. An appointment for a hearing examination was made. The examiner, using an audiometer to test Tommy's hearing, found indications of a hearing loss. Tommy was referred to an otologist (ear specialist) for a medical examination. Even after medical treatment, Tommy still had enough hearing loss to make special education in speechreading, auditory training, and speech therapy essential. His audiogram

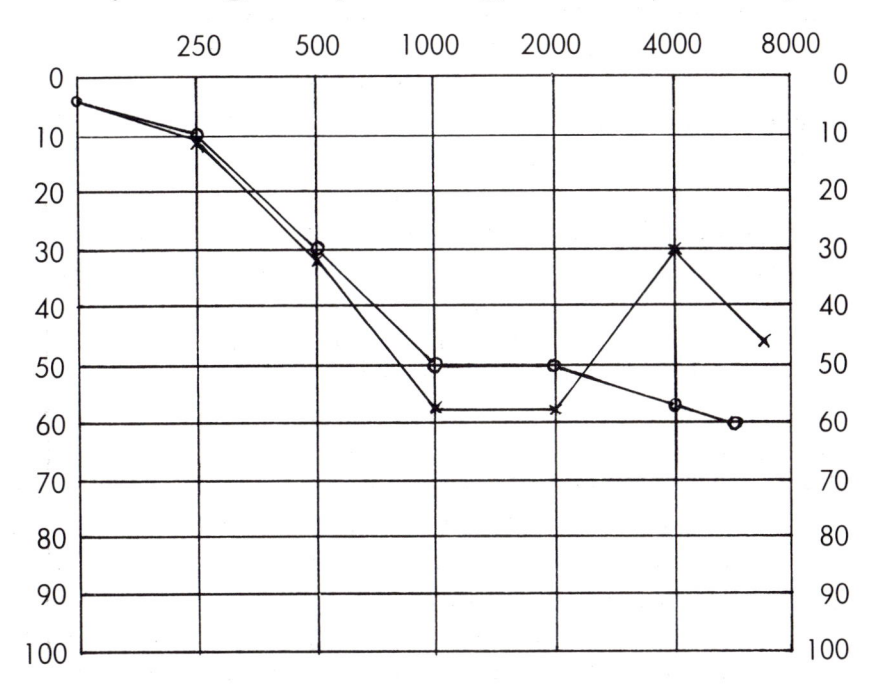

Figure 9. High-Frequency Loss

(Figure 9) shows a high-frequency loss. His speech was also affected, particulary those consonant sounds which are most difficult for the person with high-frequency deafness to hear.

Not until one loses his own hearing or has a child with impaired hearing does the importance of good hearing become apparent. With no hearing, speech cannot be heard and therefore cannot be learned without great difficulty; noises cannot be heard warning the individual of danger; music and the singing of birds cannot be heard. However, in this present-day life of mechanical activity the loss of hearing ability may serve as a definite advantage to the individual who performs some task requiring concentration. From the standpoint of social activity, the hard-of-hearing child lives somewhat isolated from his playmates.

Hearing and Speech

Perhaps hearing is more closely related to speech than to any other function of the body. The main difference between types of deafness and the hard-of-hearing condition is a matter of methods used in speech acquisition. The hard-of-hearing child may be slow in learning to talk, and may even develop defective speech sounds, but he does learn speech through hearing others talk. Whereas, the deaf child born without the ability to hear has no conception of speech or language until taught by special methods. Other deaf children, losing their hearing after speech was acquired, will need to maintain speech adequacy through speech instruction and auditory training.

All degrees of hard-of-hearing conditions exist. Some children have less than 15 per cent loss in both ears, and yet this deficiency may be sufficient to retard speech development. One young boy came to the speech clinic at Ohio University with unintelligible speech. Upon asking him to read a simple story in the reader, he mumbled as though he knew how to read. However, he grunted only the vowel sounds, indicating very few consonants. A hearing test was made, and his hearing loss was found to be only about 15 per cent loss with greater deficiency in one ear. If one ear were normal, speech could be learned satisfactorily. He probably had not developed an awareness for the consonant sounds. With special help, the boy learned how to talk distinctly.

Incidence of Hearing Problems

Examination of the results of mass testing of the hearing of school children reveals that from 2 to 21 per cent of the children have defective hearing. This variation in the number of hard-of-hearing children found in schools is probably due to the standards used in defining a hearing impairment, the apparatus used in testing, the conditions of testing, and the socio-economic status of the communities in which the testing was done.

It is estimated that 5 per cent of the school children may be hard of hearing. Of this group, one to two out of every 10 children will need special education in lipreading, auditory training, speech therapy, or class instruction in school subjects.

Because hearing handicaps do not make the child look abnormal, he is often not discovered as early as desirable for the proper educational treatment. For this reason, a hearing testing program for every child is important. The parent and teacher can also be aware of certain symptoms associated with the hard-of-hearing condition.

Rehabilitation

Many school children with hearing problems do not yet receive any medical or educational assistance. However, school superintendents are gradually developing hearing conservation and hearing rehabilitation programs.

Help has been extended to the deaf or those with severe hearing loss. It has always been more "dramatic" to help the extremely handicapped child, letting those who have slight difficulties struggle by themselves. As a result, very little has been done for the slightly hard-of-hearing child. He is often sent to the state institutions for the deaf where he has to associate with those so much worse than he is; or he may be transferred to a day school where lipreading is taught to the deaf. After a time, he returns to the regular school. Fortunately, many of the states now have legislation extending aid to the slightly hard-of-hearing child. Speech clinicians are often qualified to give special instruction to the children with impaired hearing. The local superintendent of schools should be consulted about services in the public schools.

If the school is to follow a well-organized program for the hard-of-hearing children, the following procedures should be observed: (1) hearing tests should be given every year to discover the child who may develop some hearing deficiency; (2) medical attention should be given to each child after any illness involving the head; (3) lipreading classes should be organized for those children with hearing losses of more than 25 decibels in the better ear; and (4) speech correction should be provided for those who have defective speech sounds and monotonous speech. A large percentage of the hard-of-hearing children also have speech defects, since they have had trouble hearing all of the sounds correctly. This gives the child two handicaps to overcome.

Symptoms of Hearing Loss

Before the child goes to school, the parent may want to know how to ascertain if the child has adequate hearing. These questions may be raised:

1. Does the child seem inattentive to what is being said to him?
2. Does he ever ask for words to be repeated?
3. Does he fail to answer questions?
4. Does he often misunderstand commands?
5. Does he breathe through his mouth?
6. Does he have any ear discharge?
7. Does he have a dull, monotonous, or nasal tone of voice?
8. Does he have any retardation in his work at school?
9. Was he slow in learning to talk?
10. Does he have difficulty in pronouncing sounds?

If the parent has to answer yes to many of these questions, the child may be suffering from some hearing loss. However, no conclusions should be made until professional counsel has been obtained. The classroom teacher will find the "Hearing Inventory" in the Appendix useful in checking the symptoms of the hard-of-hearing child.

If a speech and hearing clinician is employed in the local public schools, an appointment for hearing tests may be made. The

Is He Hard of Hearing

school nurse may also be qualified to give screening tests of hearing. The otologist (ear specialist) is usually equipped to administer hearing tests. If no facilities are available in the local community, write to the nearest university speech and hearing clinic for an appointment for a hearing examination. The state departments of health or education may also be able to direct you to diagnostic centers.

The family physician will advise if the child has any physical defects which may be causing the hearing difficulty. For further medical assistance, the otologist will give a detailed examination of the throat, nose, and ear to ascertain the presence of any diseased, impaired condition or growth which may interfere with hearing ability. The ear specialist will be qualified to evaluate the functioning of the physiological structures of the various parts of the ear as illustrated in Figure 10.

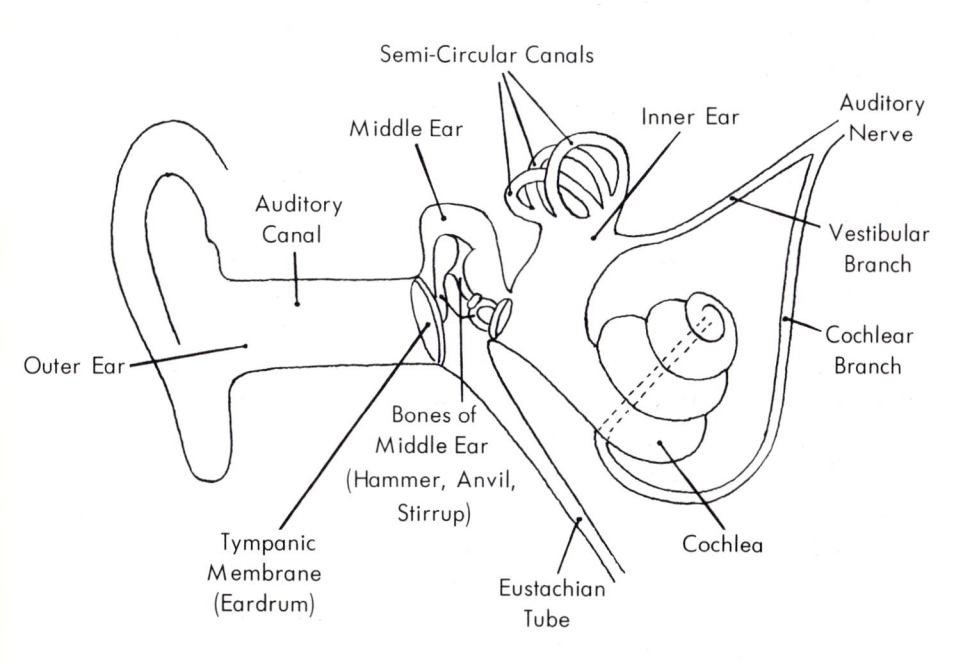

Figure 10. Sectional Diagram of the Human Ear

If the child is in school, how does he behave? Does he get along well in school subjects? Do teachers complain about his "stupidity" or "inattention"?

The hard-of-hearing child's personality or behavior does not differ greatly from the normal-hearing child. The young hard-of-hearing child often reveals some emotional instability, assumes a dominant attitude (possibly to compensate for his inferior hearing) or makes a poor adjustment in school. He frequently appears to be unhappy. The hard-of-hearing person may rate lower in leadership and aggressiveness than the normal-hearing child. Unless the child has suddenly become hard of hearing as a result of some disease or injury, the adjustment has been a gradual process. In other words, the child may have become "used to his trouble," without fully realizing his handicapped condition.

Treatment Program

After a complete diagnosis has been made, the parent should become interested in doing something about the situation if the findings reveal that the child has a hearing loss of even as little as 15 per cent in the better ear. What is to be done? In the first place, the physician should be consulted and arrangements made for the correction of any organic defects which may be producing the hearing deficiency.

If a hearing loss of 25 decibels or more in the better ear remains after medical treatment, the child may need special education in (1) speechreading, (2) auditory training, and (3) speech correction. Staff members at a speech and hearing center or individual therapists recommended by the American Speech and Hearing Association will be able to guide the child's hearing and speech rehabilitation program.

The ears hear what they can or are trained to hear. Depending upon the severity of the hearing loss, the child is exposed to many types of sounds. For instance, he listens to the radio, sound movies, and concerts. His mother reads or tells stories to him. As much as possible, the child becomes independent of lipreading or hearing aids.

Almost every hard-of-hearing person needs some training in

Is He Hard of Hearing

speech. He may have learned to talk at the normal time, but his hearing may be decreasing, and as it grows worse the speech is likely to become deficient. In such a case, speech training should begin as early as possible in order to make use of the hearing that remains. The hard-of-hearing child often has difficulty in correctly pronouncing all the speech sounds. His particular difficulties are usually with the high-frequency sounds. Some of these particular sounds are *s*, *th*, *t*, *sh*, *ch*, *z*, and *v*. The vowels *a*, *e*, *i*, *o*, and *u* are easier to hear than the consonants. However, without the consonants, speech becomes a series of noises without intelligibility. This difficulty often occurs among the hard-of-hearing children with high-frequency deafness.

Auditory training for a group of hard-of-hearing children.
Courtesy The Ohio State University.

Deaf children learn to read.

Parent Helps Child at Home

Although the parent may know little or nothing about lipreading, he can help the child to watch the lips of other people. By watching how the sounds are made, the child will soon learn how to "read talking." Moreover, the child may be taught to watch the expressions and actions of people. What child needs to know the exact words being said when the mother bids someone "good-bye" at the door? The mother may say, "Good-bye, oh, do come again!" By her very expression and manner, the child knows approximately what is said.

Observing these principles will aid the parent in teaching his child to understand speech:

1. Be sure to obtain his attention before speaking or giving a command.

2. Teach your child to watch your face while you talk. Always have a good light on your face. Speak in a normal voice and at a normal rate. Use no gestures. Avoid pointing to objects.

3. If you are not understood, repeat your instructions with different wording. Some words are more easily seen on the lips than others. For example, the child may understand "My mother and father are with me," but be unable to understand "my folks are here." Always repeat phrases or sentences instead of single words.

4. Encourage the child to speak. Sometimes the hard-of-hearing child is "stingy" with his speech. He should use sentences.

How should the child be treated at home? "Should I give my hard-of-hearing child more attention than the other children?" asks a patient mother. Just as with any other handicapped condition, too much solicitous attention on the part of the mother or father may make the child a problem to handle. He may take advantage of his parents and teachers, making the most of his handicapped condition. Certain considerations, however, should be given to the hard-of-hearing child without his realizing that he receives treatment any different from the others. Moreover, the parent should strive to accept his child's handicap in a realistic and unemotional manner in order to help the child avoid any sensitivity about his condition.

Your child should be encouraged in his school work, but never "pushed" beyond his capacity or compared unfavorably with his hearing brother or sister.

Although your child may be sixteen or older, encourage him to remain in school. More than ever, he will need education to compete in the world of hearing persons. If you need financial assistance, write to the State Department of Education, Division of Vocational Rehabilitation.

The child should be encouraged to accept responsibilities. Choose games which will help him to develop his powers of perception and discrimination, such as fitting together blocks of various shapes. Your child needs to be encouraged to play with others.

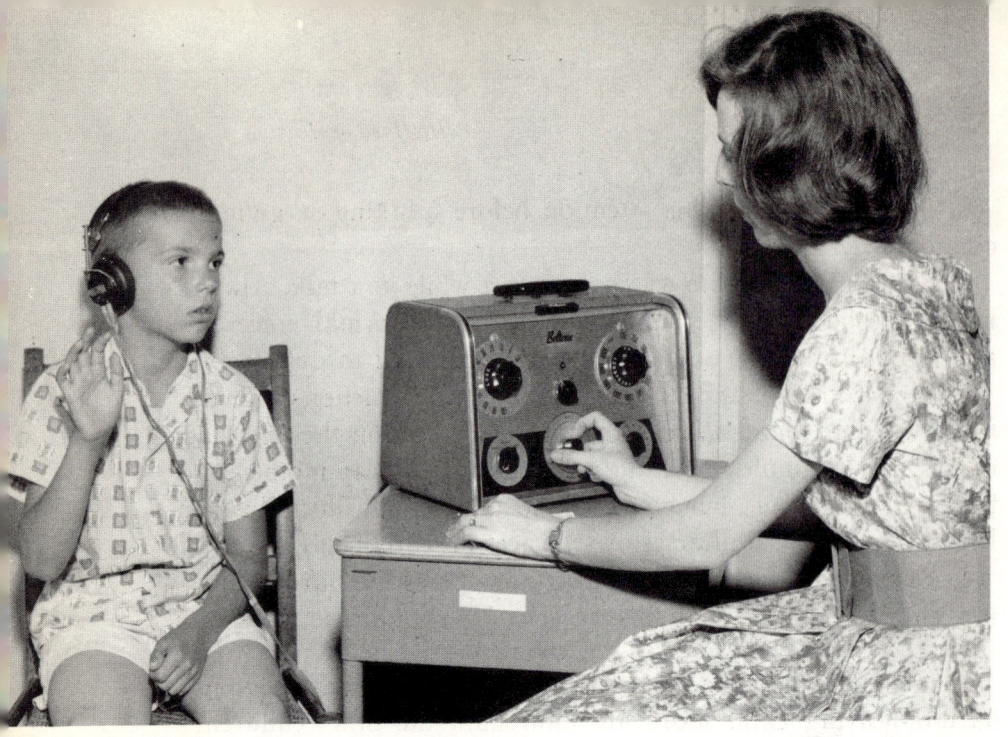

Courtesy The Ohio State University.

Testing a child's hearing with an audiometer; when a sound is heard, the child raises his hand.

Invite children to your home. A child who does not hear often plays too much by himself. Help your child to develop some hobby or skill so he will have some distinction among other children. An achievement will help to counteract any feelings your child may have as a result of his hearing loss.

Of course, the parent is always interested in how to prevent hard-of-hearing difficulties and also how to prevent the condition from growing worse. Some of the following precautions have been found worthwhile for the preservation of hearing:

1. Keeping the ear, throat, nose, and mouth in good condition.
2. Having the ears checked after each infectious disease, such as scarlet fever, mumps, and severe colds.
3. Avoiding colds as much as possible, especially the cold that "hangs on."
4. Having frequent ear tests (audiometric reports) will reveal early beginnings of hearing difficulty.
5. Teaching the child how to blow his nose.
6. Having ear difficulties treated by a physician.

Courtesy The Ohio State University.

Testing hearing of a young child with "play audiometry." Some young children need the play approach.

The School's Hearing Conservation Program

Your school officials may be doing their part in finding the children who have hearing impairment. If so, you may receive a letter stating that your child was given several hearing tests which indicated that he should be given an otological examination by an ear specialist. If the school or state does not provide a hearing diagnostic clinic, you should obtain an appointment with an approved otologist for an examination and suggestions for medical treatment.

Medical Follow-up

You should follow the recommended treatment carefully. Early and proper medical treatment can alleviate many hearing defects. A loss of hearing may be more successfully treated in childhood than at any other time. If not treated, the hearing loss may become worse. It has been estimated by reliable otologists that at least 50 per cent of adult hard-of-hearing conditions could have been prevented by early treatment.

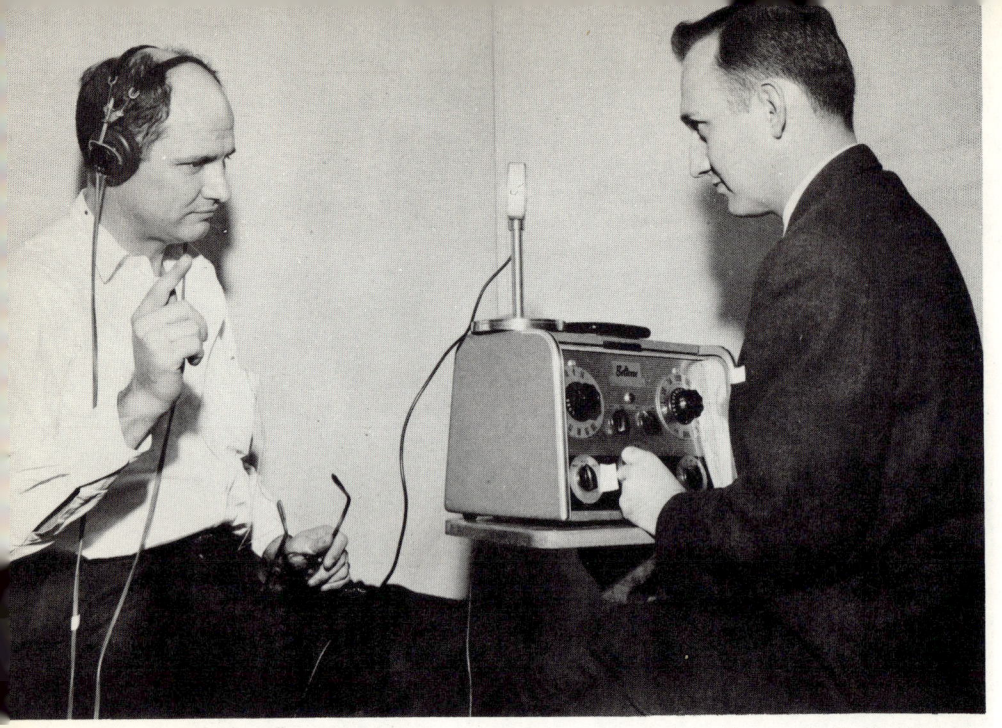

Courtesy The Ohio State University.

A parent has his hearing evaluated.

Educational Follow-up

Your school may or may not have classes in lipreading, auditory training, and speech therapy. Ask your superintendent if a speech and hearing therapist is available. Your child may need this special type of instruction two or more periods each week in order to maintain satisfactory status in his class.

Watch your child's school progress. He may need special tutoring in some of his subjects. Perhaps the teacher does not know he is hard of hearing. Visit her and talk to her about your child's difficulty. For children with serious hearing impairment, special tutoring services may be provided by the State Division of Special Education.

If no services for a hearing handicapped child are available in your community, write to the State Departments of Education and Health for guidance.

Summary

Varying degrees of hearing loss occur among the children with hearing handicaps. Some children are born deaf and so have to learn language and speech through special methods used by teach-

Is He Hard of Hearing

ers of the deaf. Other children are able to adjust to the hearing world through the use of hearing aids, lipreading, and special seat placement in the classroom.

It is estimated that approximately 5 per cent of the school children may be hard of hearing, although percentages vary from community to community according to health factors and methods of testing.

Rehabilitative services are designed to fit the needs of the child. State schools for the deaf and special day classes in the public schools for the deaf are available. When a day class for the deaf child is available, it is believed that this may be preferable to institutional placement. Other children with hearing losses may receive special lipreading and auditory training in many public schools today.

The child with a hearing loss may be inattentive, ask for repetition of words, fail to answer questions, be slow to talk, have speech inaccuracies, talk too loudly or too softly, or show retardation in school.

Any treatment program for the hard-of-hearing child should include the close cooperation with specialists from the medical profession. The school nurse and the speech therapist (if there is one) will guide the parents in the treatment procedures.

The parent is given a few suggestions in this chapter for helping the hard-of-hearing child at home. Further guidance should be sought from a speech pathologist and audiologist.

In many school communities, hearing conservation programs are in operation. Each child is given a hearing test to ascertain whether or not he has normal hearing. Medical follow-ups are usually planned. If the child is found to have a hearing loss after medical treatment, educational services in lipreading, auditory training, and speech therapy are planned.

If no hearing testing is provided in the public schools of your community, write to the State Health Department for information concerning hearing conservation programs. For educational opportunities for the deaf or hard-of-hearing child, write to your State Department of Education. Qualified speech pathologists and audiologists may be found at your state university speech and hearing clinics.

Problems and Projects

1. After seeing a presentation of one of the films on hearing, write a review. Include your reactions to the film.

2. Read and comment on the dramatic skit, "Now Hear This," which is included in the Appendix.

3. What services are available in your community for the diagnosis and treatment of the hard-of-hearing child? List and describe each service.

4. Describe the symptoms or behavior of some hard-of-hearing child you know. Estimate his lipreading ability. Does he have any speech or voice problems? If so, are they related to the hearing condition?

5. Observe and report on a visit to a class of hard-of-hearing children in the public schools or university clinic. What techniques were used? Give your reactions to what you saw.

References

Anderson, V. *Improving the Child's Speech.* New York: Oxford University Press, 1953, Chap. 11.

Davis, H.,ed. *Hearing and Deafness.* New York: Holt, Rinehart, and Winston, 1960.

Fiedler, M.F. *Deaf Children in a Hearing World.* New York: Ronald Press, 1952.

Heiner, M.H. *Hearing Is Believing.* Cleveland, Ohio: World Publishing, 1949. An autobiography of a hard-of-hearing person.

Hoversten, G. and J. Keaster. "Suggestions to the Parents of a Hard-of-Hearing Child." *American Academy of Ophthalmology and Otolaryngology,* 1959.

Johnson, W., et al., *Speech Handicapped School Children.* New York: Harper, 1956, Chap. 8.

Keaster, J. "Children With Impaired Hearing." *Speech Problems of Children.* Ed. W. Johnson. New York: Grune and Stratton, 1950.

Myklebust, H.R. *Your Deaf Child: A Guide for Parents.* Springfield, Illinois: Charles C. Thomas, 1960.

Ronnei, E.C. *Learning to Look and Listen.* New York: Columbia University, Teachers College, Bureau of Publications, 1951.

Streng, A., J.W. Fitch, L.D. Hedgecock, J.W. Phillips, and J.A. Carrell. *Hearing Therapy for Children.* New York: Grune and Stratton, 1955.

Films

Listening Eyes (The John Tracy Clinic, 924 West 37th Street, Los Angeles 7, California), 17 minutes.

Ears That Hear (Wisconsin State Board of Health, Division of Health Education, State Office Building, Madison 2), 15 minutes.

That the Deaf May Speak (Ideal Picture Corporation, 233 West 42nd Street, New York, or the Lexington School for the Deaf).

The Search: Hearing (Young America Films Inc., 18 East 41st Street, New York 17), 1955, 25 minutes.

Ears and Hearing (Encyclopedia Britannica Films, Inc., 1150 Wilmette Avenue, Wilmette, Illinois), 1950, 11 minutes.

Thursday's Children (British Information Services, 30 Rockefeller Plaza, New York 20), 1955, 22 minutes.

11
Can He Read Well?

What does the poor reader do? He may read too fast; he may read word by word, pointing as he reads; he may repeat words, trying to find the right pronunciation; he may read too slowly, hesitating on every other word; he may fail to make proper groupings; or he may omit letters as he pronounces the words. In addition to actual difficulties with the reading of the material, the child may have developed some personality problems. He may have formed an intense dislike for school as a result of his poor reading ability. He may be negativistic, stubborn, or nervous. He may cry easily, or have temper tantrums.

How Many Poor Readers?

From 10 to 20 per cent of the school population has been found to be seriously retarded in reading ability. As with speech, more boys have difficulty with reading than do the girls.

Speech and Reading

There appears to be some relationship between speech difficulties and reading abilities, although the exact nature of this relationship is not known. Common factors, such as poor sound discrimination or mental retardation, may cause both the speech and reading problems. Environmental inadequacies may also account for speech and reading deficiencies.

In a study of 300 advanced readers and a similar number of retarded readers by Jackson[1], 10 per cent of the accelerated readers and 23 per cent of the retarded readers possessed speech deviations. Yedinack[2], in a study of over 100 second-grade pupils

---

1. J. Jackson, "A Survey of Psychological, Social and Environmental Differences Between Advanced and Retarded Readers," *Journal of Genetic Psychology*, LXV (1944), 113–131.

2. J.G. Yedinack, "A Study of the Linguistic Functioning of Children With Articulation and Reading Disabilities", *Journal of Genetic Psychology*, LXXIV (1949), 23–59.

found that children with functional articulatory defects are significantly inferior in both oral and silent reading to the children with normal speaking ability.

It would appear that some relationship exists between reading and speech. More research needs to be done in this area. It seems that emphasis should be placed on speech training in the public schools with some attention to vocabulary and oral language. Before instruction in reading is given, it would be advisable to develop some adequacy in speech skills.

Reading Readiness

Reading, writing, spelling, and speech have to be learned. The child does not talk, read, write, or spell just because his parents did. It is believed that a certain area of the brain controls the activities of the language abilities; consequently, if one is out of order, the other may be.

Because of physical maturation, the child is ready to walk at a certain time, usually twelve to fifteen months. He is ready to learn speech from twelve to thirty months. Not until the child has become matured mentally and physically can he learn reading. Several authorities have agreed that the child is really not mature enough to learn reading satisfactorily until he is six-and-one-half to seven-and-one-half years old. To urge the child to read before he is ready may cause unnecessary harm.

Reading Disability—A Penalty

Since so many children have reading problems, schools often provide special instruction in reading. However, the budget or the over-crowded curriculum does not always allow enough individual attention for the child with severe reading retardation. In many instances, children have been allowed to pass reading courses and been promoted to high school and often to college without achieving adequate reading ability to do good school work. A reading handicap may cause educational failures and psychological maladjustments.

How does the child react when he finds that he cannot read as well as the others of his age? He may assume one of several different attitudes. He may accept his deficiency and not try to read. He may withdraw from activities of the class, making no attempt at all to get his school work; or he may become aggressive, expressing his reading inability by fighting, bullying, or yelling. On the other hand, the less antagonistic individual may compensate for his reading deficiency by excelling in some other subject, such as shop work, arithmetic, or drawing. The most healthy attitude for the child to take, however, is to attack the problem of reading, and with help from a well-trained teacher, learn how to read satisfactorily.

Diagnosis of Reading Problems

As with speech, reading disabilities are caused by many factors. No defect depends entirely on a single condition. Moreover, the individual who has the problem is more important than the condition itself. How does the individual react to specific conditions which seem to have produced the disorder?

Before knowing how to proceed, the person who is to help the child with his reading problem must know something about the causes of the difficulty. The reading habits of the child must be observed. In an analysis of causal factors involved in reading disability cases, many psychological tests have been devised for making the diagnosis. Any recognized psychological clinic can aid the parent in helping the child. The psychologist can give intelligence tests to ascertain whether Jimmy or Esther are mentally inferior or whether the child is particularly inadequate in language activities. Achievement tests also can be given to find at what level Jimmy is now reading. He may be trying to read material on a level too high for him. Although he is eleven years old, his reading age may only be eight years. So the teacher and parent should find material that will be easier for him and let him proceed slowly with his work. Otherwise, he will become discouraged.

The psychologist can also give tests for the eye, ear, and motor coordination. About 20 per cent of the poor readers are found to need glasses. The audiometer is used to determine the hearing difficulties of the poor reader. Approximately 40 per cent of the poor readers have partial deafness, poor auditory discrimination, or deafness for certain sounds. If the child is not alert to sounds, he will not associate sounds with the letters of the words he is reading. Consequently, his reading and spelling both may be poor.

The clinical psychologist may also find that the child has poor motor coordination. If the child falls easily or is extremely awkward, he may be poorly coordinated. Such poor coordination may cause the eyes to be ineffective in following the words, or the child may even have difficulty in pointing to the words with his fingers.

In addition to these tests, handedness, eyedness, and footedness tests may be given to determine if the child has sufficient brain dominance to control the reading activities. As with speech, reading is controlled by one side of the brain. If tests reveal that the child is right-eyed and right-handed, then the left hemisphere of this brain is supposed to control his language activities, which include reading. However, a change of handedness may have caused some hemispheric confusion. The left-handed writer often does mirror writing, and the left-eyed reader may be found to be reading upside down and backwards. One little girl in the clinic at the Hill-Young School of Speech Correction in Los Angeles drew pictures which were upside down. Such people see words and pictures in this way. It has been found that about 40 per cent of the poor readers are left-eyed. Possibly they have difficulty in adjusting the dominant left eye to the proper direction of reading material which is arranged for the normal average reader.

Besides giving the child several tests to ascertain some of the factors which may be causing the difficulty, the diagnostician must take a complete case history of the child. If the clinical psychologist takes the history, he should confer with the parents, with the family physician, and with the child's school teachers. By observation, the parent may determine if the child is weak or easily tired by his work. Insufficient sleep may handicap the child in school work. The physician may aid the parent in determining what effect the child's physical condition may have on his reading progress.

Environmental conditions, surrounding the child, may also be instrumental in retarding his reading development. Due to poor economic conditions, he may feel insecurity in his home; or he may feel emotional insecurity, as a result of his parents' quarreling continuously. These insecurities add to the child's problems and may have an effect upon his school work.

A consultation with the child's reading teacher may help to determine why "sonny" is not doing so well. Too much stress may be given to reading for speed, or to silent reading, or to oral reading. Some children learn by the silent method, but others need to hear the words pronounced aloud many times. Reading needs to be learned by sight, by ear, and by feeling. It is believed that modern teachers of reading have been teaching too much by the visual method, ignoring the importance of the phonetic training. Many children in school systems today do not even know what sounds the different letters make. Consequently, new words often have no meaning to them, whatsoever, from the standpoint of "sounding it out." It may be that a child needs to learn how to sound the letters; his hearing may be more acute than his eyes.

Treatment Program

Supposing the child needs to read better than he has been doing, what can be done? In the first place, a physician should be consulted to find out the child's physical condition. If nothing is wrong with the child's eyes, ears, glands, or health, then a reliable clinical psychologist should be found to give the psychological tests which will be helpful in determining the causes of the child's difficulty. Furthermore, the psychologist may outline a program of procedure which may be used at home, in case no arrangements can be made whereby the child is sent to the psychological clinic for individual supervision.

In planning the remedial program for the child with a reading disability, certain factors should be considered. Does the child seem to learn how to read more easily by the visual method of quick recognition of words and letters? Does the child seem to learn more readily by the phonetic method in which letters are "sounded out"? Does the child seem to learn more rapidly through the kinesthetic method, in which he traces words and later copies the word? Probably, a combination of the visual, phonetic, and kinesthetic methods should be used to enable the child to progress as rapidly as possible in the acquisition of his reading skills.

Specifically, what can the child's parent or teacher do to promote the reading skills? The child should be encouraged whenever possible. He needs individual help with his reading. Lots of interesting materials suitable for the child's reading age (level on which he can read most satisfactorily regardless of his age or grade level) should be provided. The child's abilities and interests should also be considered in choosing materials and methods. He may like to write the words on a small blackboard; he may like to typewrite the words; or he may like to play games with words and letters. Reading periods for the child should be planned systematically at regular times when the child will be least tired.

Games may be played. Reading activities are now available in many of the department stores. Picture cards may be made by pasting magazine pictures on cardboard. On other small cards, words are printed to match the pictures. The child attempts to match the pictures.

Some letters are so much alike that the young reader has difficulty distinguishing one from another. Several letters are made on small cards. A box for each sound is made. As the sound p, for instance, is made, the child looks for the letter p, and puts it in the proper box for the p's.

Another game may be called the naming game. Every letter has a name. Regarding k for instance, parents may say, "What is its name?" The child may answer, "It is k." The teacher continues in this manner: "What does the letter say? How do you make the letter?" This activity enables the child to combine all three sense avenues: seeing, hearing, and feeling. The child with speech problems is fortunate to have a teacher who uses the phonic method of teaching as attention is given to the sounds of the letters.

As has been indicated, the parent or teacher may help the child with a reading disability in many ways; however, the prevention of reading problems should also be a function of the teacher and others responsible for the education of the child. To be a "normal" reader with few difficulties, the child must have adequate intelligence, good eyes, acute auditory discrimination, good health, good enunciation and articulation, good environmental and psychological conditions, wide background of information and experience, good educational opportunities, and a "reading readiness." Reading readiness does not usually occur until the child is six or seven years of age.

Summary

From 10 to 20 per cent of the school children are seriously retarded in reading ability. Special remedial instruction in reading is often provided in the schools.

Children with speech difficulties often have reading problems. Working on one language problem may have an effect on the other. For instance, the attention to phonics in the classroom may help both speech and reading problems.

To diagnose and treat reading problems, the services of a psychologist, remedial reading teacher, and other specialists may be needed. Prognosis is related to intelligence, auditory discrimination, speech adequacy, environment, and reading readiness.

Problems and Projects

1. Describe your child's reading needs and abilities.
2. Have you attempted to help the child to read? How?
3. Discuss the factors which may cause reading problems.
4. Prepare and demonstrate one activity which may help your child to read.
5. What is the relationship of speech and reading problems? Explain how the treatment of one will help the other.

References

Artley, A.S. *Your Child Learns to Read.* Chicago: Scott, Foresman, 1953. (Guide for parents whose children use the The New Basic Reader.)

Betts, E. *Foundations of Reading Instruction.* New York: American Book Company, 1957.

Dolch, E.W. *A Manual for Remedial Reading.* Champaign, Illinois: Garrard Press, 1939. (Dolch reading cards are available at department stores and variety stores.)

Monroe, M. *Growing Into Reading.* Chicago: Scott, Foresman, 1951.

Russell, D.H. *Reading Aids Through the Grades.* New York: Columbia University, Teachers College, Bureau of Publications, 1957.

Film

Why Can't Jimmy Read (Syracuse, New York: Syracuse University, Audio-Visual Center). This film relates how Jimmy, a nine-year-old child with reading difficulties, is successfully treated.

12

Personality Adjustment

The tall, skeletal figure sat rigidly while her hands showed white knuckles as she gripped the edge of the chair. She stared fixedly at the floor through thick lenses. This was Lena. Her teachers had rarely heard her speak. Her classmates ignored her. Her parents had referred to her as "crazy," "different," or "such a disappointment."

Lena was in the seventh grade. She had average ability. She had grown rapidly and her posture was poor, but she had good skin and her hair was attractive. She was always well dressed. The speech difficulty had existed since Lena had learned to talk. The stuttering block was usually silent with an accompanying tic of the lips and chin, then followed by repetitions of sounds with irregular breathing, irregular tempo, and much cluttering.

This was a girl with many personality adjustment problems because of speech inadequacy and lack of understanding by parents and teachers. The speech clinician worked toward the restoration of confidence in Lena who felt that her "family wants to get rid of her."

"How am I to protect my child against situations and ideas which may bring harm to his personality?" is a question in the minds of many mothers and fathers. Parents, in many instances, are so involved in solving their own existence problems that the child is often neglected and allowed to shift for himself. How the child thinks and acts during his early years will determine to a large extent how he will behave in adult life.

How does your child react to the increasing tensions of the day? Is he making favorable adjustments? Do the radio or television programs have any effect upon him? Is he annoyed by your constant worry over increasing costs of living? Is he well-adjusted emotionally, so that he can meet these daily disturbances with the least annoyance? Not unless your child is emotionally upset by the situation will the effect be detrimental to his developing personality. Calmness in everyday living will do much to help him to maintain a state of well-being.

Meaning of Personality

"Just what do you mean by personality," you may ask. Personality is that something which is frequently discussed and frequently defined in various ways. It is a big word with much meaning. One might as well ask, "What or who is a person?" or "What are you?" How would you describe your child? Who is he? You may say that he is a small boy who will not behave in front of company. That may be one way you describe him at this particular time. You describe another person according to the effect his appearance and behavior have on you. Some children affect you favorably and some do not. In many instances, the child's personality is described as being good or bad according to the way he acts. However, the child tends to behave as he thinks you expect him to behave. He may act differently with various individuals. You may be surprised to find that your Johnny is the best behaved boy in school according to his teacher. He has always been a "regular demon" at home.

Your child's personality begins to evolve the minute he enters this world and continues to grow until he dies, although his major development comes during early childhood when his environment is new and full of different problems which cause him to develop his initial habits, ideas, attitudes, methods of behavior, and feelings. He attempts to adjust to his surroundings. How he adjusts will determine in a large measure how he will meet the problems in his mature life.

Your child is a reflection of those persons and things which he knows. He reveals to a certain extent your social standing, your economic status, your intellectual level, your educational standards, and your ideas and attitudes. Every person, every activity, every object, and every idea with which he comes in contact will influence his manner of response. Unfavorable stimuli may induce unfavorable responses or adjustments unless the child has been prepared to meet such conditions as they arise.

For the purpose of this discussion, the following definition will be used: Personality is the sum total of the child's physical and emotional adjustment responses to the stimulations of his social and physical environment. His inherited physical and intellectual capacities will determine in a large part how effectively he can adjust to his surroundings. However, the child's environment is very important in determining the kind of responses or behavior which will occur. Given a strong, beautiful body and a good intellect, the child can still learn to react unfavorably if his parents or his friends interfere too much with his natural desires.

When the child first comes into this world, he reacts in many undifferentiated ways. For instance, he moves all over when he moves. He cries for anything and everything. Not until he is several weeks old, do you see differentiated movements or signs of a growing personality which will have distinct characteristics of its own. How often you have heard someone say, "All babies look alike to me." It is probably due to the fact that the baby has developed no individual traits as a result of his interaction with the demands of society. As he grows older and he matures physically, he enters into the activities of life around him. His parents then begin to make demands of him, when they discover he is able to comprehend meaning at all.

Physical Characteristics

Outstanding personality characteristics already determined for your child are his general body build and his intellect. If he has inherited a strong body and a good mind, he has a good beginning toward his being able to adjust to his environment satisfactorily. If his physique develops rapidly for his age, his teacher and classmates may demand more of him. He appears to be older than he is. On the other hand, if he is small for his age others may treat him as though he were younger. He may be the "cute" member of the crowd. Consequently, your child's general appearance may determine the type of response he receives.

In addition to physical beauty and size, the cleanliness and dec-

Personality Adjustment

oration of the body may influence reactions to the child. If the boy is dirty with tousled hair, his teacher may wish to disregard him although she does not do so openly. The boys and girls, however, may not be so charitable. As a result, your boy (granted he is the unfortunate member) may respond in an unfavorable way as far as his personality is concerned. He may become aggressive and try to get even with the fellows for treating him in a mean way, or he may retire within himself and become very shy and backward. The type of temperament which he has will determine largely how he will react or adjust to this baffling situation.

The healthy condition of the body will also lead to favorable responses, since health makes the boy feel good. He is happy and easily pleased. Whereas, if he does not feel well, or is poorly fed, he may develop some bad habits. He may whine incessantly. He may be irritated easily. Injury to the body which leaves a handicap of any kind will also determine, in many instances, how others will react to him. He responds in the way he thinks they expect him to act, although this type of response may not be favorable for healthy personality growth.

Ductless glands also play an important part in the child's personality makeup. If the glands are not functioning adequately, behavior reactions result which appear in definite types of personalities in many instances. What are the chief glands as far as your child's personality growth is concerned? The pituitary gland which lies at the base of the brain may be controlling your child's growth to such an extent that he is too large or too small, too fat or too thin. His abnormal size often causes his adjustment to his environment to be difficult. He is frequently made unhappy by "taunts" received from his friends. They call him "skinny," "fatty," "spider," or "shorty."

The second gland of importance to your child's personality adjustment problems is the thyroid. It is situated at the front and sides of the neck below his "Adam's apple." It may be acting too well, or not well enough. Too much thyroid secretion causes the child to be unduly active, restless, and tense. His reactions will thus be made accordingly. Too little thyroid secretion may make the child inactive, depressed, and intellectually dull. Proper functioning of these glands will do much toward making the child happier in his adjustments. If any treatment is undertaken, it should be under the direction of the physician, who understands endocrinology.

Intellectual Factors

In addition to a good physical makeup, your child is greatly helped if he has a normal amount of intelligence. Intelligence is something with which the child is born just as he may be born with blue eyes or with black hair. There is not much you can do about it, if he is mentally deficient. However, several factors may cause the child to appear to be retarded mentally, even though he is not. For instance, he may be delayed in speech, emotionally upset, or underdeveloped, glandularly. Moreover, his early childhood surroundings may not have furnished him adequate stimuli to develop his thought processes.

If your child has inherited a superior intelligence, he will be much more adequately prepared to solve his problems than the child who has a low grade of intelligence. If unexpected situations arise, your intelligent child will respond quickly and with imagination. He will be able to adjust more easily than his retarded classmates. The mentally retarded child, however, can be trained to meet some situations adequately, but the unexpected problem may cause him much difficulty since his imagination is lacking.

Summary

A general discussion of the meaning of personality is presented in this chapter. Personality is defined as the sum total of the child's physical and emotional adjustment to the stimulations of his social and physical environment. The inherited physical and mental abilities will determine to a great extent how effectively the personality operates in relationship to others; however, unfavorable environmental factors may have serious effects upon the adjustment of an intelligent and physically beautiful body.

As the child grows, he meets many situations which cause him degrees of concern according to his ability to meet the problem. Your child's personality is what you, his teachers and friends, make him. When he comes into the environment, he has the body, the intellect, the temperament that you gave him. Now that he is in the world, he has to act, think, and talk the way that his parents and teachers expect. The way he meets other boys and girls, the way he behaves in school, and the way he plays with his brothers and sisters are all results of the forces interacting to produce his particular personality.

Problems and Projects

1. What does personality mean to you? Describe your child's personality. What effect has the speech problem had on him?

2. How does mental ability affect the development of the personality? Relate your answer to a child you know.

3. How does physical appearance affect the personality? Relate your answer to some child you know.

4. Observe a child with speech difficulties on several different occasions. Describe his behavior, physical appearance, and probable mental ability.

5. What standards of speech do you have for your child? In what way might your expectations and demands affect the personality of the child?

References

Hymes, J.L. "A Healthy Personality for Your Child." U.S. Children's Bureau Publication, No. 337. Washington: Government Printing Office, 1952. (A discussion aid accompanies the publication.)

Travis, L.E. and D.W. Baruch. *Personal Problems of Everyday Life.* New York: D. Appleton-Century, 1941.

13

Educational Adjustment

Richard, although normal in intelligence, had difficulty adjusting to situations at school. Because of his cleft-palate speech, the children ignored him and would not play with him. He was often destructive at school and attempted to obtain attention in undesirable ways. He repeated grades; but as the speech clinician worked with him, his social and educational adjustment improved.

Tommy was only five years old, but he was operating mentally as though he were eight years old. He found the small group of five-year-old speech-handicapped children with whom he received speech therapy non-stimulating. When the clinician discovered his superior intelligence, she understood why he appeared bored. Although he was only five, the approach to therapy needed to be more direct and less playlike than that used for the "normal" five-year-old children. Because of his high intelligence, Tommy learned to correct his defective sounds readily.

Surveys have indicated that the speech-handicapped child is often retarded in school placement a year or more than the child with normal speech. Children with speech problems may hesitate to recite in class for fear of riducule by classmates. If speech is unintelligible, no attempt at speech may be made. Sometimes, children are penalized because speech is not understood.

Education Begins at Birth

As soon as the child enters this world, he begins his education. In a short time, he learns that a nipple means something that stops his hunger pangs. He learns to cry when he needs or wants attention. He babbles and coos. Gradually, he learns that "ma-ma" means his mother. Speech is learned—words and then sentences.

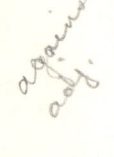

For children who do not learn speech, controlling the environment is often difficult and frustrating. Some adjust to situations more readily than others. How a child meets a problem will depend in a large measure upon his mental maturity or intelligence.

What Is Intelligence?

As with the definition of personality, many attempts have been made to define intelligence. What is it? Simply stated, it is that innate ability of the child to learn and to adjust himself to the problems of his environment. He must be able to think, to solve difficult problems, to reason out situations, and to evaluate methods of achieving goals.

"Mental capacity," "mental ability," "mental age," and "intelligence" are all terms used in describing a person's ability to learn. The chronological or actual age of the child based upon his birthday may be five years; whereas, his mental age or level of learning ability may be only four years. Consequently, this particular child might be retarded mentally approximately one year.

About 60 out of every 100 children are normal in intelligence. These children adjust reasonably well in schools where the "average" child usually receives the major attention. Consequently, they meet the ordinary demands of society without too much trouble.

However, the child who is much above or below the normal range in intelligence or learning ability often has problems. The gifted child is often understimulated in a class planned for the "average" child; the "slow-learning" child is overstimulated. Neither the gifted nor the slow-learning child is able to make the most use of his abilities in a situation not geared to his capabilities.

As a parent or teacher, your goal should be to work toward helping the child to make the most use of his abilities. For the "slow-learning" child, the objective should not exceed his reach. If the goal does not conform with the capabilities of the child, frustration and unhappiness may result. The child with superior intelligence must be challenged with extra projects or he may become bored or a behavior problem in a class designed for children with average intelligence.

If your child is exceptionally bright, provide opportunities for him to use that intelligence; otherwise, he will misdirect his energies. If he is mentally retarded, help him to learn activities suited to his level of performance.

The wise parent will "face the issue" and meet the problem of mental superiority or mental retardation with a constructive attitude. Obviously, all parents want the best for their children. They often expect too much. To accept the fact that one's own child is mentally retarded is difficult. After adequate testing and observation, the decision may be: "Your child is retarded and will be slow in school." The psychologist or counselor will guide you in planning a program suitable for your child.

If you think that your child is unusually bright, or possibly you are wondering if he has adequate intelligence, you should make some attempt to find out if he is doing suitable work for his mentality. Each child must be treated as an individual. Not until the child is doing the work that is entirely within his range of ability will he be a happy person.

If he is in school, go to the child's teacher or principal. Talk to her. Tell her your problem. In some cases, school authorities are hesitant about telling the parents about the actual score the child received in an intelligence test. This hesitancy exists only because of concern over possible misunderstanding on the part of parents and others about the interpretation of the score. If you cannot obtain the exact score, you can find out if the child is doing school work adequately suited to his ability.

If the child is not in school, go to a reliable clinical psychologist for guidance.

Speech and Intelligence

Speech is closely related to mental ability. In general, mental age is much more significant in influencing speech proficiency than chronological age. About 60 per cent of mentally retarded children have one or more deviations in speech.

Very little evidence is available to guide us concerning the effectiveness of speech therapy for the mentally retarded speech-handicapped child. It is assumed that therapy, to be effective at all, must be given as much as possible throughout the school day by the regular classroom teacher and at home by the par-

Courtesy The Ohio State University.

Stimulation of language in a group of speech-handicapped children.

ent. For this reason, there needs to be close cooperation between the clinician and the teacher and parent. The teacher of the slow learner needs to learn as much as possible about how to stimulate the speech production of the child. In some states, the teacher of the slow learner is required to take at least one course in speech correction.

Attention needs to be given first to language development rather than to the correction of specific sounds. The association of speech with daily activities is often a beginning.

The children with normal intelligence can usually show reasonable progress in the speech therapy program in which the clinician visits the school only twice a week. The bright child who has speech deviations can usually correct a sound error very quickly after once learning what has been wrong and how to make the correct sound.

Testing of Intelligence

At the university speech and hearing clinics, psychological screening tests are often given to ascertain the probable learning ability of the speech or hearing handicapped child. Both verbal and performance tests are given.

An example of a verbal test is the Ammons Picture Vocabulary Test in which the child is asked to point to one of four pictures on a card which most nearly fits the word spoken by the examiner. The examiner says, "Show me 'man'." The child points to the picture which he thinks represents a "man." The total number of words recognized by the child is converted to a mental age.

The Goodenough Draw-a-Man Test is an example of a performance test. The child is asked to "draw the best man you can." Through a standardized scoring procedure, the mental age is determined.

If the child is found to have low scores on the screening tests or some discrepancies between the two types—verbal and performance—further testing is often recommended.

Stanford-Binet Test. Over 50 years ago, the first testing of intelligence was tried by a Frenchman named Binet, who became the co-author of the present individual intelligence test called the Stanford-Binet. The French people found a need for some method of finding out what children were incapable of learning in school. Not until schools were made public and required compulsory training, did they feel the need for the testing of intelligence.

However, when all children were required to go to school, certain students were found to be unhappy and unable to adjust to the demands of the school situation. Problems of truancy arose. As a result, mental testing was originated.

In the Stanford-Binet test, many problems and tasks are given to the individual to solve. After performing the series of tasks, a certain score is reached. This final score is called the "I.Q." or intelligence quotient, which means an index to the child's intelligence or ability to learn.

TABLE III   Levels of Intelligence

Description	Range of I.Q.'s
Genius or near genius	above 140
Very superior	120-140
Superior	110-120
Normal	90-110
Dull normal	70-90
Morons	50-70
Imbeciles	25-50
Idiots	below 25

Other tests are also used by psychologists to determine a child's mental ability. Often, more than one test is given. In schools, group intelligence tests are often given.

Levels of Intelligence

Ability to learn, based on mental ages and intelligence quotients, is often classified in terms of various categories. The children with superior intelligence may be rated as superior, very superior, or genius; children with average intelligence may be considered normal or dull normal; children with defective intelligence may be rated as morons, imbeciles, and idiots. The scores may range from below 25 for the idiots to above 140 for the genius or near genius class.

The Normal Child. Since there are so many children with normal or nearly normal intelligence, the major interest in most of the schools is with the normal child who has adequate intelligence for most of his needs. We need to help these children to make the best use of their intellectual capacities. The normal child should be encouraged to do the best that he can, although you should never expect him to do more than he is mentally capable of doing. Many behavior problems result from overstimulation by parents. Dad may say, "You've got to make all 'A's' next time if you want that bicycle."

The Mentally Retarded Child. Before the child is six years of age, several factors may be responsible for causing his delay in developing normal intelligence. For instance, delayed speech, emotional blockings, or inadequate glandular functioning may retard the child's mental development. After the child learns speech and attains a vocabulary with which to think, his intelligence quotient will often increase as much as twenty or thirty points. Proper emotional retraining by a trained person will also aid in releasing emotions which have tended to retard his intellectual growth. If glandular deficiency is suspected, let your family physician give the child a basal metabolism test which will show if too much or too little thyroid is the disturbing factor.

In addition to these causes of mental retardation, heredity has been stated by most authorities to be the main factor in causing mental deficiency. In some instances, birth injury, paralysis, and disease have been known to cause backwardness. If your child happens to have an inferior mental capacity, as a result of any of these latter factors, nothing much can be done to help him to gain more intelligence. The best procedure to follow is to accept the fact as well as you can, and then to find a way to help your child to be trained sufficiently for him to care for himself and possibly to earn his living. What he can do depends upon the degree of his intelligence. In all events, begin specialized training early for your child if he is found to be mentally retarded.

The mentally deficient child should learn how to get along with other children; he should learn to keep himself neat and clean; he should learn certain habits of conduct acceptable to society; he should become as independent as he is able; and he should have some preparation for a place in the world's work.

The level of instruction presented in the regular classroom is often too difficult for the retarded child. Unless the teacher can give the slower pupils individual attention, these children will experience inferiority, frustration, and failure. Special education classrooms are provided in many school systems for children who are retarded. These special classes present instruction on a level of difficulty at which the retarded child is able to participate with some success. If you are hesitant to place your retarded child in such a room, visit a special class teacher and watch her work with the children. You may see some definite advantages for placing your child in the special classroom.

How does the child with low mentality differ from another child who has a high rating? In the first place, children with inferior intelligence are frequently slower in physical development than are the normal or superior children. They are slower to begin their walking. They are usually slow to begin talking.

In the second place, low mentality causes the child to be poor in making adequate adjustments in social situations. He will often cling to old ways. He has little imagination in how to get out of trouble. He wants to play by himself.

In the third place, the boy or girl with inferior ability is slow to improve with instruction. He may learn, but his learning progresses at a very slow rate compared to that of his brighter friends.

The Superior Child. What are the chief characteristics of the child with superior mentality? Terman, in his studies of intelligence among children, found the following tendencies for the superior children: curiosity, alert understanding, extensive information, good memory, early speech development, and comprehensive vocabulary. Other studies have indicated that superior children usually have better health and better physiques than those of the inferior group. A bright child may show powers of leadership, but he is not always the leader of the group. He may be very shy and still brilliant.

A leader needs to have initiative, willingness to work, and ability to work with people plus his natural intellectual power. A bright child usually has a keen emotional drive to do things. He wants to go to school. If he makes up his mind he wants an education, nothing will stop him.

Perhaps your big problem right now is a child with superior intellect. What are you to do with him? How are you to treat him? Perhaps he is only six years old, and yet he thinks and acts like a ten-year-old. Usually, the intellectual growth in such cases develops faster than the emotional and the physical growth. Consequently, the problem becomes complicated.

Since his emotional and physical development are not usually on a par with his intellectual ability, the superior child should be allowed to play with children of his own age, so he can learn to make the social adjustments he will need later if he is to use his intellectual capacities to the best advantage. His physical work, of course, must be at his own age level since his strength has not developed as rapidly as his mentality.

Educational toys suitable for the mental age level should be provided. If he is mentally ten years old, but only six, then his toys should require the thought of the ten-year-old. You should talk to your boy as though he were a ten-year-old, since he thinks as a boy of that age.

Instead of rushing the superior child through school before he is emotionally ready for adult life, provide opportunity for him to use his ability in other ways. For instance, he can be given extra work at school if no special facilities are provided in your school for the exceptional children. In order to make a superior grade he must do a certain amount of work. In many schools, no attempt is made to take care of the special abilities of the superior child. Consequently, he often uses his energies in unprofitable ways. The superior child must have suitable activity and enough of it!

You may have to help the child to maintain a proper attitude toward his superiority. He may soon discover that he is able to do things that his classmates cannot do, especially if he is kept in a room with all types or degrees of intelligence. He may brag, "Johnny sure is dumb! I got through an hour before he did and didn't have a thing to do! So, I just threw paper wads at that Wallace girl!"

Of course, the child need never know his score in intelligence until he is old enough to understand its significance. Moreover, he should never hear his superiority discussed at any time. If you should even discuss his unusual ability in front of relatives, the child may soon learn of it through the avenues of gossip. You can also help him to maintain a normal attitude toward his superior mentality by calling attention to activities of other children who are able to do some things which he is unable to do. In this way, you may keep your child from developing that unfavorable superiority complex which may lead friends to dislike him as a person.

Summary

Educational adjustment is usually dependent upon the intelligence of the child who is normal physically and emotionally. Approximately 60 children out of every 100 are normal in intelligence. These "normal" children adjust to an educational program usually designed for them. The child much above or much below the normal range of intelligence will often have difficulties adjusting to the average school curriculum of studies and activities.

Each child needs a program which is best suited to his individual mental abilities. Urging the child to exceed his ability will lead to frustration and unhappiness. The bright or gifted child may lag behind his normal classmates in the program designed for the average child because of inadequate challenges.

The development of speech adequacy is closely related to mental ability. The gifted child has a larger vocabulary, longer sentences, and fewer speech problems than his less intelligent friends. The mentally retarded child is usually slower to talk than the bright child, although this is not always true.

An understanding of the effect of mentality upon speech adequacy and progress in speech therapy is important so that expectations will not exceed the capabilities of the child.

In his adjustment to intellectual problems, the child's personality emerges according to his ability to meet each situation. The normal child reacts as almost all children tend to react. That is the meaning of normality—reaction in an average or normal manner.

However, each child with a normal intelligence has differences. One child may be better in literature than another. A second child may be good in mathematics. Likewise, the child with superior intelligence varies considerably from other children with superior ratings. Each child has particular skills and abilities.

The big challenge to the parent is to help the child to make the most use of his particular general intellectual level and specific talents. If the child appears to be unusually good in shop work and his intelligence is "average," why try to make him a doctor? If he likes literature and is good at it, why make him an engineer? Each child needs to be encouraged and guided according to his abilities and interests. He will appreciate your help later when he has become happily adjusted in work that he likes and is able to do well.

Problems and Projects

1. Visit a special class for slow learners in the public schools. Listen for speech problems. Write a discussion of what you saw and heard.

2. Read and report on one of the references.

3. Talk with a speech clinician about therapy for the child who is mentally retarded. Report on your interview.

4. How is your speech-handicapped child affected by his mental development? Is he doing his best or are his goals too high for his capabilities?

5. How is intelligence related to speech problems? Why does the speech clinician need to know something about the child's learning ability?

References

Irwin, R.B. "Oral Language for Slow Learning Children." *American Journal of Mental Deficiency,* LXIII (1959), 32–40.

Kirk, S.A., M.B. Karnes, and W.D. Kirk. *You and Your Retarded Child.* New York: Macmillan, 1956.

Loewy, H. *The Retarded Child.* New York: Philosophical Library, 1951. (A guide for parents and teachers.)

Strang, R. *Helping Your Gifted Child.* New York: E.P. Dutton, 1960.

Strazzulla, M. "A Language Guide for the Parents of Retarded Children." *American Journal of Mental Deficiency.* LIX (1954), 48—58.

Film

Class for Tommy (Bailey Films, Inc., 2044 North Berendo, Hollywood 27, California), 25 minutes. A special class for mentally retarded children in the Los Angeles Public Schools.

14

Emotional Adjustment

Parents often complain that their children have behavior problems. Among normal children, many behavior disorders exist. In trying to adjust to a world with many demands and changing situations, the child often reacts in unfavorable ways according to the adult's idea of the proper conduct. Adults are likely to forget that the child's emotions have to develop as well as his body.

One child may be so shy that he will not talk when others are around, or another child may be so forward that he shows off all the time. Individual differences in personality plus parental and environmental control often determine behavior differences. To the parent or teacher, the boy who throws paper wads or fights is a much greater problem than little Willie who sits in his seat and says nothing. However, little Willie may be the most serious personality problem in the room, and the unhappiest boy in the school, although he causes no trouble at all.

Various types of behavior problems have grouped themselves into two general classes: the withdrawal and aggressive types. Little Willie was an example of the withdrawal type. He was unhappy, possibly because he did not feel well, and as a result withdrew from the strain of class participation. Across the aisle from Willie may sit another boy, who shows his unhappiness by general mischievousness.

Among the quiet retiring children are those who are trying to escape from some unfortunate situation which irritates them. They may feel inferior in some respect, and so try to remain as obscure as possible. The aggressive fellow shows off by fighting, "throwing temper tantrums," stealing, lying, talking too loudly, or by playing truancy from school.

Emotional Adjustment

Speech Problems and Behavior

Many speech authorities have often wondered which came first, the behavior problem or the speech disorder? Unfavorable behavior may occur as the result of the speech problem. In some instances, the behavior reaction may be responsible for causing the speech problem. The mother may be so willing to do everything for the child, that the child never feels the need for speech, and consequently, doesn't talk—thinking, thereby, to gain more attention. Whatever the reason, behavior disorders seem to have a definite relationship to speech handicaps.

One twelve-year-old boy came to the speech clinic unable to talk distinctly enough for the clinician to understand his name. When asked any questions, Bobby would shrug his shoulders, turn his head away, and look at the clinician from the corners of his eye. At first, the clinician thought the behavior problem would be so severe that no speech work could be attempted immediately. Even the psychologist found that Bobby felt no trust for any of his helpers. However, after he felt assured that he would receive some help for his speech, he was willing to cooperate. With each success, he became happier. After a few months, he found that he could talk as well as any of the other fellows— and what a difference in his personality! He changed from an antagonistic little fellow to one who was willing and cooperative.

Mary Anne also came to the clinic. She was accompanied by her quiet, non-aggressive mother. Mary Anne was seven years old and could not talk. No one could do anything for her! If any attempt was made to help her, she would fight. She deliberately did things to annoy her parents and teachers. She tried to dominate everyone. She apparently was determined that no one would teach her to talk. As a result, much time was needed to conquer her strong negativistic attitude before any speech re-education was attempted. Possibly her mother was too weak and ineffectual with her disciplinary measures for a child with such a dominant will.

Another case of delayed speech with strong, aggressive tendencies was that of a bright eight-year-old boy. He was so strong in his reactions against his inability to speak that he would "hit anyone with no provocation at all." However, after receiving some help with his speech, he gradually became emotionally controlled.

No discussion of behavior problems would be complete without an introduction to the spastic girl, Betty. To understand Betty's life is to know a great deal about what may happen to any handicapped individual when the mother does too much for the child. Betty was already sixteen years old—so helpless, apparently, that her mother had to wait on her "hand and foot." Betty was even fed every spoonful of food by her mother. As a child, Betty had developed a spastic condition which required her to wear braces, but she was still able to walk, play, and do practically everything for herself. Here's the "catch." As she grew older, she found that she was different from the other girls. She could not dance. She could not wear beautiful dresses like her girl friends. As a result, she wept—her mother felt sorry for her. From then on, the child grew dependent on the mother, allowing her to do anything and everything. This girl was even jealous of her dad's few hours with her mother. Not until the mother was persuaded to take the child away from home, and leave her alone for several months, did the girl show any improvement. Now, that she knows that her mother "is wise to her true condition," the girl has grown independent and capable of doing things for herself.

Causes of Behavior Problems

Numerous reasons may be attributed to the beginnings of behavior problems in children. Each behavior reaction will show its manner of manifestation according to the personality of the child. The naturally quiet child will become more retiring than ever; whereas, the social child will become more domineering and bold than ever. Among the causes for behavior problems are listed physical disorders and handicaps. A child with poor health will often be more irritable than the healthy child. Poor glandular development may cause retardation in intellectual activities, plus various types of behavior reactions which may prove unfavorable. Consequently, the physician should be consulted in regard to the physical health and condition of the child's body. Any physical irregularity may be causing the child's behavior problem.

In addition to physical weaknesses and handicaps, intellectual capacities may not be found to fit the demands of the child's environment. His mentality may be too low for him to cope with the problems of his playmates. He is unhappy. His parents also may insist that he make all "A's" when he is capable of making only a good "C." Any child should be required to do the work he is capable of doing, but he must not be urged to exceed his capabilities. The strain will make him unhappy, and behavior problems may result.

Then, there is the child who is too brilliant for his environment. No one requires him to do enough. His mother and father give him toys intended for a three-year-old when he is capable of playing with toys suitable for a child two years older. It is to the parent's advantage to know whether the child is much above or below the normal range of mental ability. Either the very dull or very bright child may become a behavior problem if appropriate activity is not provided.

What about the child's environment? Is it as satisfactory as possible? The pleasant atmosphere of the home will help the child to become adjusted to his particular problems. Discord between the parents has often caused unfavorable behavior reactions among the children. Undesirable behavior frequently comes from homes with emotional tension. Moreover, poor economic status of the family has been found to be a contributing factor; if the child is inadequately housed or poorly dressed, he may run away from home or mix with unfavorable playmates.

Obvious handicaps, such as reading disability, speech defect, hearing deficiency, spasticity, and crippled conditions will often be responsible for the behavior problem. The child is unable to adjust himself happily to his environment, and as a result he develops some unfavorable social reactions. In the case of reading disability, the child finds that he is not able to read as well as the others in his class. He feels unhappy: "What shall I do? I'll just show those kids! My mother will take me out of school and she'll help me!" The mother then becomes quite sympathetic with the child's condition. She even talks about it a great deal in the presence of the child. The child takes advantage of the situa-

A Speech Pathologist Talks to Parents and Teachers

tion, and soon finds that he is receiving lots of favors that his other friends do not receive. However, he is also developing some infantile mannerisms that belong to a child much younger than he is. He could pass for that "spoiled young brat of the Jones."

Treatment of Emotional Problems

What can be done with the child if he has some behavior problem? In general, the first step should be to eliminate the causes. Parents should consult the doctor to find out if the child is physically normal. If his physical state is satisfactory, psychological factors should be investigated. Is too much attention given a younger child? Is discipline too severe? In many cases, remov-

The mother encourages the speech-retarded child to adjust emotionally to frustrating situations by doing things with the child.

Courtesy Ohio University.

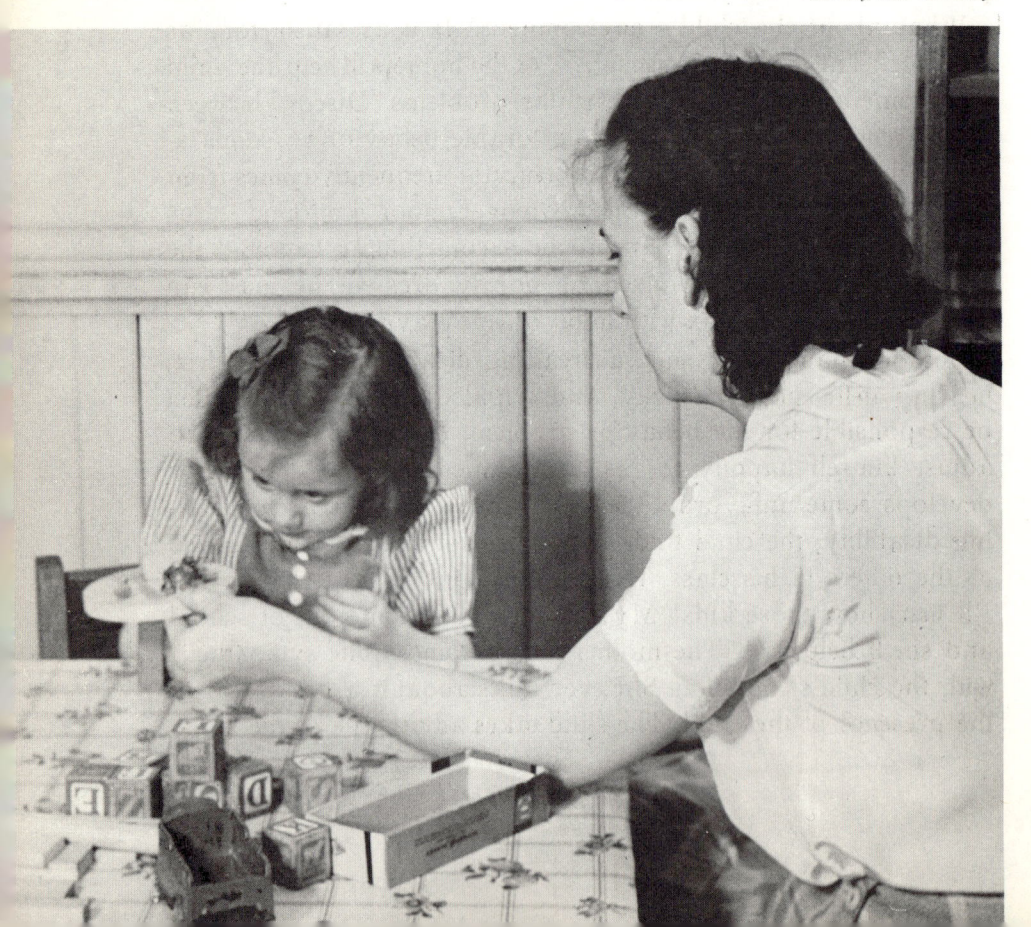

ing the cause will be sufficient to remove the behavior misdemeanor.

Negativism and Disobedience

All children ordinarily go through a period, usually from two to five when they react in a negative way to most demands. They are gradually evolving that "self" which wants to be an individual with rights. Consequently, a certain amount of negativism is a healthy sign that the child is developing in a normal way. However, he may be continuing his period of negation beyond the normal period. He may become so disobedient that he is a problem, and if so, certain measures for re-education may need to be taken.

Certain factors may be causing the child's tendency toward extreme negativism. For instance, are the child's fundamental needs satisfied? Does he receive enough affection?

Are unreasonable demands made at unreasonable times? How consistent is the discipline? Maybe, the child is told today that he may play with the dog in the house, but tomorrow he cannot. He, consequently, may become confused as to the correct procedure. Perhaps, the parents do not agree on their treatment of the child. Dad may say yes, but Mother says no. There must be cooperation between parents if the child is to respond favorably.

If the negativistic behavior is serious, some punishment may be needed. However, corporal punishment must never be used as the parent is often too angry when the "whipping" is administered. In many instances, ignoring the child's stubborn actions will work. If direct means need to be taken, withdrawal of certain privileges may work.

Jealousy

The usual cause for jealousy is the entrance of a baby in the household to usurp the small child's place in the realm of his mother's love. He wants the attention which is suddenly given to someone else. He is angry!

What are the usual symptoms of a jealous child? He may whine, cry, or even steal and fight to obtain the attention which he thinks he is not getting. His need for love and affection are being thwarted, so he thinks. He is demanding that he be loved. The aggressive child probably will fight, steal, or have temper tantrums to get his needs fulfilled; but the quiet child may become more timid than ever and develop extreme inferiority feelings. The timid child usually causes so little trouble that no one becomes alarmed about him, but the aggressive jealous fellow demands attention at once. However, both children are in need of help. At least, the little fellow who fights and yells is expressing his feelings and having some relief; whereas, the silent unhappy boy keeps all of his feelings "bottled up." In reality, the silent boy is the more serious problem of the two children.

The jealous child is often "mean" to the person who tends to disregard his feelings or activities in any way. He may show a special attachment to his mother, even though he is obstinate and unhappy with her. He may even hit her, try to trip her, or slap her to get even with her for not giving him more attention or for not allowing him to do what he wants. The jealous child often is highly nervous and in need of more sleep than the average child.

Some of the usual causes of jealousy are the introduction of a new baby into the family, the interference with the child's usual method of doing things, the unfavorable comparisons made with a brother or sister, inconsistent punishment, and too much domination by the parents.

In the case of unfavorable comparisons being made among several children of the family, the youngest child often is jealous of an older brother, because mother may say to him frequently, "Do you see what your brother John can do? You ought to do it that well, too." Little brother feels like hitting big brother for being such a nuisance in his life of security.

In order to overcome extreme cases of jealousy, the parent may need to examine his methods of treating the child. It may be that his methods are without fault. However, each parent should raise these questions: (1) Have I dominated him too much with inconsistent methods of punishment? (2) Have I prepared him for the coming of the younger child? (3) Am I making unfavorable comparisons with another child in the family? (4) Am I partial in my treatment of the children? Each child wants to receive his share of attention. If one child is loved, the other one has to receive his love, too.

Temper Tantrums

Temper tantrums cause a lot of annoyance to parents at embarrassing times. A temper tantrum is an expression of anger. The child may kick, scream, or wave his arms when he dislikes what is being done to him or when he is not getting his way with someone or something. Frequently, a temper tantrum is a means of his getting what he wants. Consequently, he may resort to that method if he has found that it works.

Probably one of the best methods of treating the temper tantrum is simply to ignore it if that is at all possible. Then afterwards, explain to the child that he can obtain what he wants only when he acts as other people act. After he has performed the strenuous temper tantrum several times with no results, he may stop.

However, if ignoring the situation is impossible as is the case many times, the child must be picked up bodily and carried to some room where he can be isolated from the others. He can be told that he must be placed by himself as he is disturbing the other people who want to work or read.

Insecurity

Insecurity usually occurs as a result of lack of affection and economic sufficiency. Tension in the home may also make the child feel insecure or unwanted. Divorce or parental separation will add to this feeling.

Perhaps the best way to overcome some of this feeling of insecurity, inferiority, and inadequacy is for the child to engage in activities suited to his abilities and likes. Allow him to achieve several successful performances. Praise him! That will give him confidence and fill him with a feeling of adequacy. He will feel, "I am able to do this as well as anyone else!"

You must be careful to make the child independent too. As long as he depends upon you, he will have a feeling that he cannot do anything by himself. If he stutters, he may look to you to do his talking for him. Let him do his own talking! He will never overcome stuttering (often a symptom of the child's feeling of inadequacy) unless he relies upon his own powers. He must meet the situation realistically.

Fear

Fear is an emotional element which is common to all people. A certain amount of fear in any situation is necessary for the protection of self against harm. Each child should be afraid to cross a street when many cars are racing back and forth. The development of fear responses takes place as the child matures intellectually and learns more about his environment. Many of his fears also develop as a result of the observation of fear reactions of older people. In addition to learning fears from other people, the child who is insecure often fears more than the child who has a feeling of adequacy.

Some of the common fears of children are concerned with dogs, high places, loud noises, dark places, and meeting strange people. Some of these are natural fears which result from a sense of protection of oneself. Others are acquired from people. A child may be threatened to do something. "If you don't do this, I'll put you in a dark closet where there is a bogey man!" Early fear conditioning takes place as a result of such threats.

In order to help the child to develop normal fear responses, the parents must check themselves for giving abnormal fear reactions. They must also aid the child toward attaining a satisfactory feeling of independence and self-sufficiency, so that he will not be afraid to attempt performances. The timid child will be afraid of strangers, afraid to climb tall structures, afraid to try anything different. The strong, confident child usually will attempt many new activities without fear of consequences.

Another way to help the child to remove abnormal fear reactions is to explain to him that there is nothing to fear. For instance, you can explore with him some fear object, such as the dark, and show him that there is nothing to hurt him.

Summary

In general, the growth of independence and responsibility will do much toward helping your child to become the unique personality that he needs to adjust adequately to all situations involving fear, anger, and love. Parents can help to create suitable environmental surroundings so that the child may develop into a well-adjusted personality.

All children have varying degrees of behavior problems. Observation of speech-handicapped children in homes and clinics indicate that they may have more behavior problems than those children without speech problems. The frustrations, fears, and inability to communicate of the speech-retarded child or the stutterer would be enough to result in behavior problems. The protective parent may add to the problem.

Besides the possibility of speech disorders, other factors may cause behavior problems. These causes may be poor health, excessive goals for mental ability, discord in the home, reading disability, hearing loss, crippling condition, or oversolicitous parents.

In the treatment of emotional problems, the parent or teacher needs to seek the counsel of the physician and psychologist. If the child has a reading or speech problem, the speech pathologist will be able to help. Such factors as poor vision, poor hearing, or poor health must be ruled out.

The treatment of any specific behavior disorder is based upon the cause. If possible, through observation and keeping a diary, the parent may be able to determine when the behavior is likely to occur. This procedure will lead to the discovery, possibly, of the irritant in the child's life.

To remove or reduce the irritating factors which produce behavior problems will also serve favorably to aid the speech-handicapped child on the way to adequacy in communication.

Problems and Projects

1. Keep a diary of the behavior of a child with a speech problem over a period of one week. What particular problems appeared? Do you feel these problems are related to the speech inadequacy?

2. Discuss your point of view concerning "Discipline." In what way may the method of discipline affect speech?

3. Evaluate one of the films on behavior problems. (This film may be presented as part of the parent education course.)

4. Discuss why you might expect a child with speech problems to have behavior disorders.

5. Prepare several questions concerning behavior problems. How would *you* answer them?

References

Baruch, D.W. *New Ways to Discipline.* New York: McGraw-Hill, 1949.

——————. *Understanding Young Children.* New York: Columbia University, Teachers College. Bureau of Publications, 1949.

English, O.S. and S.M. Finch. "Emotional Problems of Growing Up." Chicago: Science Research Associates, 1951.

Hymes, J.L. *Discipline.* New York: Columbia University, Teachers College, Bureau of Publications, 1950.

Ilg, F. and L.B. Ames. *Child Behavior.* New York: Harper, 1955.

Kellogg, R. *Babies Need Fathers, Too.* New York: Comet Press, 1953.

Mayer, J. *Getting Along in the Family.* New York: Columbia University, Teachers College, Bureau of Publications, 1949.

Travis, L.E. and D.W. Baruch. *Personal Problems of Everyday Life.* New York: D. Appleton-Century, 1941.

Films

Children's Emotions (New York: McGraw-Hill Text Films). A light touch is used to show the problems of childhood.

It's a Small World (New York: Communication Materials Center, Division of Columbia University Press, 413 West 117th Street), 45 minutes. Shows the lives of a group of nursery school children in some of their adjustment problems with each other and the teacher.

Meeting Emotional Needs in Children (Vassar College, Department of Child Study). This thirty-three minute film is distributed by the New York University Film Library, 26 Washington Square, New York 3. Shows typical behaviors of children in the elementary school. Some situations in the home which intensify problems are shown. Suggestions to parents and teachers are given.

Preface to a Life (New York: Communication Materials Center, Division of Columbia University Press, Office of Special Projects, 413 West 117th Street). This film shows how adult behavior may influence the developing behavior of children.

15

Social Adjustment

Donny, a five-year-old boy, was brought to the speech clinic as a "stutterer." Children had recently made fun of his speech. According to the mother, "Donny would rather play alone and has shown no apparent liking for other children." He refused to stay in a Sunday School class. He liked looking at pictures and being told stories, working with clay, singing along with the phonograph, and looking neat.

He depended upon his older brother for all social relationships. According to the mother, the child was stubborn and difficult to handle. The parents differed in methods of discipline, the father believing in firmness and the mother using the lax approach. The mother's social life was inadequate. She had not been anywhere since a television set was purchased two-and-one-half years ago. The factors in Donny's speech problem were related to friction between the parents, their overconcern for the speech, and Donny's competition with his seven-and-one-half-year-old husky brother.

The recreational life of the entire family needed to be expanded with a less tension-producing atmosphere at home. The program of therapy at the clinic included work with the parents in order to help them understand the problems which were affecting the child's speech. Working with other children in a small group helped Donny to achieve desirable social relationships which lead to relaxation in speech situations.

Your child is what society makes him! If he lives in a poor community "below the tracks," he learns the language of the streets. He acts as the boys with whom he plays. The socially accepted manner of conduct in your vicinity is usually your son's standard of action to follow.

If your child is a member of a rich society where maids, butlers, gardeners, and chauffeurs are employed, then he may be a "well-behaved little fellow" who has had special training in speech, music, and manners. He may be more dependent, however, than the poor boy across the tracks since he has so much more done for him. His period of dependence is usually extended over a longer period of time.

Janie, who had many speech problems, came from a well-to-do home in Beverly Hills, California. She heard the speech of a Japanese gardener, Hungarian grandparents, and maids who spoke slovenly English. Her parents were too busy to spend much time with her, so she did not really get the social advantages of associating with her well-educated and cultured parents.

Then there was Benny, a twelve-year-old boy who stuttered. His parents were naturally much concerned about him. They indicated that: "We have given him everything a boy could possibly want. He has a pony. We gave him a television set for his room. What more could we do?"

The mother taught at the university and the father traveled. The boy saw little of his parents. It appeared that he needed more association with them—he wanted personal attention from those who loved him. To develop speech adequacy, children need proper social relationships which add to their feelings of security.

Personality and Speech

Your child may well say, "I am what you have made me. I am a part of all I have heard; I am a part of all I have seen; and I am part of all I have felt!" Not only do you as his parents play an important part in the emergence of the child's self, but so do his playmates and other people in his immediate community play important roles.

From the social standpoint, personality may be defined as that expression of an individual's inner thoughts, feelings, attitudes, and desires. Personality has little way of finding expression except through the medium of speech. People with whom your child associates call forth from him certain expressions. Your boy may have to uphold his rights in a game. He may say, "No, that isn't the way it is done." Through speech, evidence is given that your son has a personality which is fair, honest, and sportsmanlike.

When friends call to see you, your child usually reacts toward them through speech, He may say, "I like them." You find out what he thinks of your friends. At school, he tries to answer the questions which the teacher asks. He uses speech in communicating information. Friendliness and kindness are expressed through speech. He may call to his friend, "Bill, why don't you come over after school tonight and play ball with me."

In many ways, therefore, speech is a direct expression of one's personality. Several writers have indicated that personality is speech. A person is often known by what he says and how he says it.

Effect of Speech Inadequacies on Social Acceptance of Child

How does your child's speech affect your friends? Does he speak distinctly? Does he use baby-talk which irritates many people who think you should have helped him to outgrow it long ago? Does he whine for everything that he wants? Does he talk in a hoarse voice that is annoying? Does he substitute sounds, such as saying, "gog" for "dog"? Maybe, he uses a language of his own which no one can understand except his brothers and sisters who are near his own age.

As you can readily see, many of these factors concerning speech do much toward telling others about the type of personality your child has. For instance, if he whines continually, they may suspect that he is "spoiled," and accustomed to getting what he wants after he whines long enough.

Perhaps, you have been guilty of using poor speech habits yourself. Do you talk distinctly, slowly, and in short sentences so that the small boy or girl can understand you? Is your voice pleasant, or do you scream at the child? Frequently a parent vents his wrath by yelling, "Now, didn't I tell you to stop making so much noise?" The child may become angry, too, and he yells! Everyone becomes irritated! Slow, calm speech helps to maintain well-adjusted lives in the home.

Speech defects may have a definite effect upon a child's social

Courtesy The Ohio State University.

Deaf children learn to adjust to others in a social situation. Learning to talk helps in social adjustment.

personality. A child with a severe articulatory defect is handicapped because no one can understand him. He is often ignored. Consequently, he may withdraw from social situations or become aggressive. Stutterers, as a group, are often shy, nervous, and unsocial individuals. Social situations are usually avoided.

Another type of speech irregularity which may concern you is the retarded development of your child's speech. Maybe, he is past three years of age and does not talk. Maybe, he is five years of age and talks unintelligibly. A child with either type of difficulty is unhappy. He does not enjoy playing with other children. He has no means of expressing his emotions, desires, and thoughts adequately. Instead of words, he uses gestures and noises. If not understood, the child may have a temper tantrum or simply withdraw completely from the social situation. The reaction of the child to the frustration will depend upon his personality.

Bobby, a five-year-old boy who did not talk except for "mama" and "uh-huh," was an unhappy child. He was afraid of other children. He obtained all of his needs through a language of gestures. In the rehabilitation of this child, the parents with the cooperation of the speech therapist gradually introduced Bobby to the society of other children. At first, it was trips to the park where other children played, to Sunday School, and then he was enrolled in a nursery school with a small group of children. This procedure along with play-therapy approach to speech and encouraging independence in the child at home led to adequate speech within six months. This boy changed from an unhappy lad who was not known to have smiled to one who was happy in his relationships with others.

Cultural Influence Upon Child's Social Personality

Your child's social personality is also influenced by the type of conduct he sees. Certain customs have already been established before he entered the group. It is his duty to perform according to what his parents and friends expect. The child is largely what society makes him!

What is right and what is wrong? This is an old question which has often been debated and discussed. According to different people and different environments, certain ideas or habits are considered wrong in one group; whereas, the same ideas or habits may be considered right in another community. The problem for the child is to conform to the rules set down by his immediate leaders. He learns the rules of moral conduct principally by speech. He grows confused many times when he sees actions which do not conform to the words he has heard regarding right and wrong. He finds that it is very easy to talk about being "good" but it is very hard to "act" as a good boy.

In a civilized society, the child has his goals already set for him in many instances. He is expected to go to school at a certain age. Going to church is also expected in many homes. The child finds that he can do some things, but he cannot do others without causing criticism.

As far as he is concerned, he does not understand the real reason for the rules of moral conduct. He has been told that it is wrong to steal, lie, or cheat, but he cannot quite realize why it is wrong to do these things, since he receives a certain amount of pleasure from doing them. So until your child reaches a certain age of mental maturity, he may operate on what is known as the "pleasure-pain" principle, in which he does what he likes to do until he is punished. If he is hurt enough times for doing what he has enjoyed doing, he may decide it is better to do as society demands.

Personality Adjustment and Attitudes

Important to your child's personality adjustment is his attitude toward certain elements in his environment. Of course, the child needs to mature mentally and emotionally before his attitudes are too well set. His ideas and reactions are very much the same as those of his parents. He usually believes as his parents do. However, his attitudes are developed during childhood and his parents and teachers aid quite definitely in ascertaining the types of attitudes he will have as an adult. He will probably develop attitudes which you want him to have if you have them yourself and also act in accordance with them.

What is an attitude? It may be defined as that characteristic method of reacting to certain ideas, objects, or persons. An attitude indicates the manner in which your child will probably react to situations. If he likes his teacher, he will do better work for her. He will even take her flowers and, maybe, an apple. If he doesn't like her, he may draw ugly pictures of her, or do mean things to her.

Your child should have proper attitudes toward the important questions of reality, security, authority, and change if he is to become that well-adjusted personality. In the first place, he should not be afraid to face reality in any situation. Dodging the issue will never make a strong character. He must do a certain task if it must be done even though he doesn't want to do it. If he can meet the disagreeable tasks as a boy, then he is more likely to meet the serious problems of adulthood satisfactorily. His attitude must be one of: "This is my job! I must do it!"

He must have an attitude of confidence. He must feel that he is secure in his work. If he is sure of himself, then he will act with more assurance. He believes in himself! This attitude will color his reactions to members of his social group, as well as the reactions of others to him.

His attitude towards authority is also very important to his developing social reactions. Does he have respect for his parents and teachers? If he believes in his parents and teachers, he will probably conform to the expected rules of conduct without resistance.

Adjustment to Changing Society

In this age of rapidly changing activity, the child also needs to learn to adjust to change. How are we to know how to train children for adulthood when we do not know what kind of life they will have in 20 or 30 years from now? Probably the most satisfactory type of adjustment to such a problem is to educate the child to become accustomed to new ideas and methods of doing things. Help him to understand that changes are constantly occurring. He needs to be ready to adapt himself to new environments and to new ideas. If he can adjust to elements of change during childhood, then the problems of later years should not be too complicated. A well-adjusted child, usually, should be expected to become the well-adjusted adult regardless of the new problems encountered.

Summary

The people who meet your child will have important effects upon how his social personality develops. Personal attention and love from parents is more desirable than all of the physical comforts which money can buy.

One's personality is best expressed through the medium of speech. Thoughts, feelings, desires, and attitudes are expressed to others. A person is often known by what he says and how he says it. The speech-handicapped person is penalized in social relationships. He may not communicate at all. If he does, he may be misunderstood or ridiculed.

Standards of conduct may be difficult for the young child to understand. The attempt to make the child "perfect" before he has matured enough leads to unnecessary frustrations and behavior reactions.

The development of interpersonal relationships which are satisfactory will give confidence to the child in social situations. An

Social Adjustment

attitude of self-confidence will affect the reactions of others to the child.

In all factors concerning the child's social personality, you as his parents are very important. To you, he looks for guidance in his choice of right and wrong; to you, he listens as he learns about proper attitudes toward people, ideas, and objects; and to you, he turns for help when he is unable to speak adequately.

To be the happy, well-adjusted social personality, your child must express himself well through speech, he must adjust himself to the moral requirements of his society with the least amount of emotional conflict, and he must attain proper attitudes toward his social and physical environment.

Problems and Projects

1. Describe the social life of your child. In what way do you feel the people he meets help him?

2. In what way is the social life of a child affected by a speech handicap? Relate your answer to a child you know.

3. How can parents or teachers help children make friends?

4. Observe children at school, on the playground, or in the clinic. Report on the behavior and speech of at least one child as he relates to others.

5. Discuss how "perfectionism" in matters of moral conduct or discipline may affect the child's developing social personality.

References

Menninger, C.W. and W.C. Menninger. "How to Help Your Child Make Friends." Reprint from *Parents Magazine.* Chicago: Association for Family Living.

Baruch, D.W. "Learning to Live With Other Children." *Parents and Children Go to School.* New York: Scott, Foresman, 1939, Chap. 12.

Film

Shyness (National Film Board of Canada: New York University Film Library, Press Annex 41, 26 Washington Place, New York 3). Shows how parents and teachers can bring about changes in children's attitudes.

Appendices

Appendix One 150
    Selected References

Appendix Two 152
    Testing Materials

Appendix Three 157
    Exercises for Use in Practice of Voice and Articulation

Appendix Four 159
    Original Playlets for Parent-Teacher Groups

Appendix Five 180
    Suggested Programs for Parents and Teachers

Appendix Six 185
    Case History Sketches of Children With Speech Problems

Appendix Seven 190
    National Agencies

Appendix One: Selected References

For the Parent Group Leader

Auer, J. and H.L. Eubank. *Handbook for Discussion Leaders.* New York: Harper, 1947

Brown, A.C. and S.B. Geis. *Handbook for Group Leaders.* New York: *Woman's Press*, 1952.

Eckert, R.G. *Handbook on Parent Education.* Bulletin Vol. 19, No. 5. Sacramento: California State Department of Education, 1950.

Faegre, M.L. *Children Are Our Teachers.* Children's Bureau Publication, No. 333. Washington: Government Printing Office, 1949.

Hymes, J.L. *Being a Good Parent.* New York: Columbia University, Teachers College, Bureau of Publications, 1949.

For the Clinician Group Leader

Chapin, A.B. "Parent Education for Pre-School Speech Defective Children." *Journal of Exceptional Children*, XV (1949), 75–80.

Fiedler, M.F. *Deaf Children in a Hearing World.* New York: Ronald Press, 1952.

Irwin, R.B. "Parent Education in the Speech and Hearing Program." *Speech Teacher*, III (1954), 169–176.

———. "In-service Training: Teachers and Parents." *Speech and Hearing Therapy.* New York: Prentice-Hall, 1953, Chap. 9.

Johnson, W., et al. *Speech Handicapped School Children.* New York: Harper, 1956, Chap. 2.

Lillywhite, H. "Make Mother a Clinician." *Journal of Speech and Hearing Disorders,* XIII (1948), 61–66.

Rheingold, H.L. "Interpreting Mental Retardation to Parents." *Journal of Consulting Psychology*, IX (1945), 142–148.

Schuell, H. "Working with Parents of Stuttering Children." *Journal of Speech and Hearing Disorders*, XIV (September, 1949), 251–254.

Symonds, P.M. *Dynamics of Parent-Child Relationships.* New York: Columbia University, Teachers College, Bureau of Publications, 1949.

Travis, L.E. and D.W. Baruch. *Personal Problems of Everyday Life.* New York: D. Appleton-Century, 1941.

Utterback, W.E. *Group Thinking and Conference Leadership.* New York: Rinehart, 1950.

Wood, K.S. "Parental Maladjustment and Functional Articulatory Defects in Childhood." *Journal of Speech Disorders,* XI (1946), 255–275.

———."The Parent's Role in the Clinical Program." *Journal of Speech and Hearing Disorders,* XIII (1948), 209–210.

For Classroom Teachers

Backus, O.L. *Speech in Education: A Guide for the Classroom Teacher.* New York: Longmans, Green, 1943.

Eisenson, J. and M. Ogilvie. *Speech Correction in the Schools.* New York: Macmillan, 1957.

Fessenden, S.A., R.I. Johnson, and P.M. Larson. *The Teacher Speaks.* New York: Prentice-Hall, 1954.

Irwin, R.B. *Speech and Hearing Therapy.* New York: Prentice-Hall, 1953.

Johnson, W., et al. *Speech Handicapped School Children.* New York: Harper, 1956.

Ogilvie, M. *Speech in the Elementary School.* New York: McGraw-Hill, 1954.

Pronovost, W. *The Teaching of Speaking and Listening in the Elementary School.* New York: Longmans, Green, 1959.

Rasmussen, C. *Speech Methods in the Elementary Schools.* New York: Ronald Press, 1949.

Van Riper, C. and K.G. Butler. *Speech in the Elementary Classroom.* New York: Harper, 1955.

Appendix Two: Testing Materials

HEARING INVENTORY*

I believe the pupil listed below has some hearing impairment. I have checked the child's symptoms to the best of my ability.

Name of pupil .... Class ....
Age .... Birthdate .... School ....
Address .... Telephone ....

I. Physical symptoms:
   1. Frequent earaches ......
   2. Running ears ......
   3. Faulty equilibrium ......
   4. Chronic colds ......

II. Speech and voice symptoms:
   1. Omission and substitutions of certain sounds of speech ......
   2. Mispronouncing common words ......
   3. Other speech defects ......
   4. Voice lacking in intonation pattern ......

III. Behavior reactions in the classroom:
   1. Requests for repetitions of words ......
   2. Turns one side of head (better ear) toward speaker .....
   3. Inattentive in class discussion ......
   4. Watches teacher's lips ......
   5. Shows strain in trying to hear ......
   6. Unusual mistakes in taking dictation ......
   7. More than normal use of hands to make wants known ......
   8. Frequent mistakes in following direction ......
   9. Low achievement for age ......

IV. Some signs that may indicate hearing impairment:
   1. Irritability ......
   2. Child appears more intelligent than work indicates .....
   3. Temper tantrums ....
   4. Inferiority complex ......
   5. Child is tense ......
   6. Child sometimes appears dull ......

Signed ....
Subject taught ....

---

*Courtesy *The Bulletin of the National Association of Secondary School Principals*, XXXIV (1950), 27–29.

Appendix Two

SPEECH INVENTORY*

I believe the pupil tested below has a speech problem. I have filled out the following questionnaire to the best of my ability.

Name of Pupil .... Class ....
Age .. Birthdate .... School ....
Address .... Telephone ....

I. Articulation:
   1. Can hardly understand him ......
   2. Omits certain sounds ......
   3. Uses "baby-talk" ......
   4. Substitutes wrong sounds for right ones, such as w for r ......
   5. Has a foreign accent ......
   6. Has "sloppy" speech ......
   7. Distorts certain sounds ......
   8. Protrudes tongue for s, z sounds ......
   9. Sounds which appear inaccurately made:
     p, b, m ...... hw, w ...... t, d, n ...... h ...
     y ...... k, g, ng ...... f, v ...... th ......
     l, r ...... s, z ...... sh, zh ...... ch, j ......

II. Voice:
   1. Usually has weak voice and can hardly be heard in class ......
   2. Has very monotonous voice ......
   3. Is too breathy when talking ......
   4. Is throaty and guttural ......
   5. Has husky, hoarse voice ......
   6. Voice is usually too loud ......
   7. Sounds too nasal to me ......
   8. Is too high pitched ......
   9. Speech lacks variety and life ......
   10. Usually talks in a whisper ......

III. Fluency:
   1. Usually talks too fast ......
   2. Usually talks too slowly ......
   3. Repeats initial sounds, syllables, words, and phrases ......
   4. Blocks sometimes and can't get words out ......
   5. Speech is jerky ......

IV. Other Problems:
   1. Has cleft palate ......
   2. Has cerebral palsy ......
   3. Appears to be hard of hearing ......
   4. Very poor reader ......
   5. Avoids speaking in class ......
   6. Appears tense and uncomfortable much of the time ......
   7. Has symptoms of nervousness ......
   8. Usually shy ......
   9. Frequently too aggressive ......
   10. Does not cooperate well in the group ......

                   Signed ....
                   Subject taught ....

*Courtesy *The Bulletin of the National Association of Secondary School Principals*, XXXIV (1950), 27–29.

PARENT'S REPORT

Child's Name .... Date ....
Please answer questions as fully as possible. Use the back of the page if necessary.
1. What sounds has your child worked on during the term?
....
2. Improvement has been noted on which sounds? ....
3. Has the general understandability of your child's conversation changed? ....
If so, how? (Please give specific words or situations.) ......
....
....
4. Have any others outside of the immediate family noted any change in your child's speech?........................
....
5. Has your child changed (behavior and personality) during the term?...
If change noted, can you account for this change? ....
....
....
6. What effect has speech therapy had on your child? ......
....
....
7. Other comments ....

                        Signed ....
                              Parent's Name

List of Words to Use in Making Picture Articulation Test

Put one picture on a card or page.
1. Consonants made with the lips.
    p — puppy, pig, pie, apple, cup, cap
    b — baby, bed, boat, boy, book, tub
    m — man, hammer, arm, comb
    hw — wheel, whistle, white
2. Lip-teeth consonants.
    f — foot, face, fire, finger, elephant, telephone, leaf, knife
    v — violin, valentine, violet, seven, television
3. Tip-of-tongue consonants.
    voiceless *th —* thumb, three, bathtub, birthday, teeth, tooth, bath, mouth

Appendix Two

voiced *th* — use two pictures, one larger than the other, and say: "Which is larger: *th*is or *th*at?" feather, father, mother, brother
4. Tip-of-tongue against teeth ridge consonants.
   t — tooth, tub, tire, butter, kitty, letter, white, feet, meat
   d — dog, doll, duck, radio, ladder, head, red, bed
   n — nut, knife, man, gun, spoon, wagon
   l — letter, ladder, lip, lady, leg, lamp, lake, yellow, balloon, ball, doll
   r — rabbit, rug, red, radio, rake, carrot, car, tire, bear, chair
   s — soup, sun, bicycle, ice cream, face, bus, mouse, house
   z — zoo, zebra, roses, scissors, eyes, nose, ears, cheese
5. Tongue-blade consonant.
   sh — shoe, shirt, sheep, shovel, shell, dishes, washing, dish, fish
   zh — televi*si*on, mea*s*ure
6. Tongue-front consonant.
   y — yellow, yard, yawn
7. Tongue-back consonants.
   k — cow, cake, comb, key, can, cup, candy, cooky, book, cake
   g — gun, girl, gum, wagon, buggy, dog, rug, pig, egg
   ng — finger, donkey, ring, tongue
8. Tongue-point and tongue-blade consonants.
   ch — chicken, chair, cheese, church, pitcher, kitchen, teacher, peach, match, watch
   j — jelly, juice, jumping, soldier, engine, bridge, orange, jar
9. Blends.
   br — bread, breakfast, broom, brother
   dr — drum, dress
   tr — truck
   kr — ice cream
   gr — green, grass
   pl — plum, plate, play, plant
   fr — friend
   st — store, stop, step, star
   sp — spoon, spade

sk — skate, sky, school
sm — small, smile
sl — sleep, slide
10. Vowels.
sock, sack, bed, face, chick, sheep, chalk, cup, church, goat, hook, soup, kite, house, toy, mule

Paragraphs for Quick Survey of Speech Problems

The passage may either be read by the subject or repeated after the examiner. Since most of the sounds are represented, the examiner may record specific sound deviations in the speech. General intelligibility, voice quality, and rhythm may also be noted as the person reads the passage of connected speech.

MY GRANDFATHER

You wished to know all about my grandfather. Well, he is nearly ninety-three years old; he dresses himself in an ancient black frock coat, usually minus several buttons; yet he still thinks as swiftly as ever. A long, flowing beard clings to his chin, giving those who observe him a pronounced feeling of the utmost respect. When he speaks, his voice is just a bit cracked and quivers a trifle. Twice each day he plays skillfully and with zest upon our small organ. Except in the winter when the ooze or snow or ice prevents, he slowly takes a short walk in the open air each day. We have often urged him to walk more and smoke less, but he always answers, "Banana oil!" Grandfather likes to be modern in his language. (From *Speech Correction* by C. Van Riper, Prentice-Hall, 1954, pp. 178–179)

A DAY AT THE FARM

My mother and I went to the farm. Sally did not go. She had to go to school. Mother drove the car. It was a red Dodge. When we got to the farm, we were hungry. But Grandma did not have dinner ready. So we helped. Mother set the table. We looked for some jelly. Grandma cooked the eggs—three of them. I put some bread and butter on the table. Soon dinner was ready. We sat down. We gave thanks for our food. We ate and ate. Grandma was glad we came. We stayed all day. (From *Speech and Hearing Therapy* by R. B. Irwin, Prentice-Hall, 1953, pp. 32–33)

Appendix Three: Exercises for Use in Practice of Voice and Articulation

For Practice of Short Phrases

Speak the speech,/ I pray you,/ as I pronounced it to you,/ trippingly on the tongue;/ but if you mouth it,/ as many of your players do,/ I had as lief the town-crier spoke my lines.
Hamlet, Shakespeare

✻ ✻ ✻

I will buy with you,/ sell with you,/ talk with you,/ walk with you,/ and so following,/ but I will not eat with you,/ drink with you,/ nor pray with you.
The Merchant of Venice, Shakespeare

✻ ✻ ✻

Studies serve for delight,/ for ornament,/ and for ability.
Of Studies, Bacon

✻ ✻ ✻

Reading maketh a full man;/ conference a ready man;/ and writing an exact man.
Of Studies, Bacon

✻ ✻ ✻

For Practice of Vowels—Prolongation of Sounds

Alone, alone, all, all alone,
Alone on a wide, wide, sea.
The Ancient Mariner, Coleridge

✻ ✻ ✻

Blow, winds, and crack your cheeks! rage! blow!
King Lear, Shakespeare

✻ ✻ ✻

A horse! A horse! my kingdom for a horse!
Richard III, Shakespeare

Double, double, toil and trouble;
Fire burn and cauldron bubble.
Macbeth, Shakespeare

❋ ❋ ❋

The day is cold, and dark, and dreary;
It rains, and the wind is never weary;
The Rainy Day, Longfellow

❋ ❋ ❋

A rainbow in the morning
Is the Shepherd's warning;
But a rainbow at night
Is the Shepherd's delight.
Old Weather Rhyme

❋ ❋ ❋

She left the web, she left the loom,
She made three paces thro' the room,
She saw the water-lily bloom,
She saw the helmet and the plume,
  She look'd down to Camelot.
The Lady of Shalott, Tennyson

❋ ❋ ❋

Appendix Four: Original Playlets for Parent-Teacher Groups

That Others May Talk

(Playing Time - 12 to 15 Minutes)

Now Hear This

(Playing Time - 15 to 20 Minutes)

by

Kenneth R. Greenburg[*]

---

[*]Kenneth R. Greenburg wrote these plays while he was a student at The Ohio State University as part of a course in *Speech Correction Methods* under the direction of Ruth Beckey Irwin. They are herewith reproduced by his kind permission. They were written for and will be found effective at Parent-Teacher Association meetings or similar gatherings.

That Others May Talk

Cast of Characters

MODERATOR, *off-stage voice (or visible)*
MR. RANDOLPH, *principal of school*
MISS SCHAFFER, *assistant principal*
SECRETARY, *to Mr. Randolph*
DELORES WINTERS, *about fifteen years old*
MISS JOHNSON, *English teacher; efficient, good-natured, popular*
MISS BAKER, *school speech and hearing clinician*

MODERATOR: Just what is speech and hearing therapy? What do we consider a speech disorder? Who are qualified to deal with such problems? And what can you, as a parent or as a teacher, do to help the child with a speech or a hearing problem?

These questions, and many more, will be answered in this, the first in a series of programs designed to inform you about the role the speech and hearing clinician plays in our public school systems today. It is the intent of these programs to further acquaint you with the many services rendered by the State in providing adequate and necessary educational opportunities. To begin with, speech and hearing therapy, as it suggests, is therapeutic and private instruction for those people who are bothered by either a speech or a hearing problem. We must first, then, decide just what is meant by a speech disorder. It has been stated, and widely agreed upon that "speech is defective when it deviates so far from the speech of other people that it calls attention to itself, interferes with communication, or causes its possessor to be maladjusted." To state this in another way, we could say that when our speech causes the listener to pay as much, if not more attention to the way we speak, rather than to what we say, a speech problem exists.

Within the past......years, the field of speech and hearing therapy has come into its own. Today,......trained and certified speech and hearing clinicians are holding positions in ......'s public schools. ......Universities throughout the State provide instruction to potential clinicians. The need for more trained clinicians is yet great; however, through the help of recent State aid, the supply of such trained personnel to carry on this work is increasing. The problem of speech disorders in our schools today is perhaps the greatest challenge for our educators. They have accepted this challenge and are attempting to meet the needs of the handicapped school children.

Perhaps we can best understand the work and the need for speech and hearing therapy by a story that could very well take place in your community. Let us look into the office of Mr. Wilber Randolph, the principal of Centerville High School. And remember, Centerville High could just as easily be your high school. Talking to Mr. Randolph is Miss Schaffer, the assistant principal.

Curtain

SCENE: *The office of the school principal — Mr. Randolph. It has the usual desk, chairs, hat rack, etc.*

(Knock sounds from door on right)
MR. RANDOLPH: Yes—come in.
Enter Miss Schaffer
MISS SCHAFFER: I don't want to disturb you . . . .
MR. RANDOLPH: *(Stands)* That's quite all right. Sit down. What can I do for you? *(Sits as Miss Schaffer takes chair)*
MISS SCHAFFER: *(Miss Schaffer sits at chair facing desk)* It's about the "Americanism Essay Contest."
MR. RANDOLPH: I see. *(Relaxes in chair)*

MISS SCHAFFER: Well, the committee has finally chosen a winner.

MR. RANDOLPH: Good, good. What's the person's name?

MISS SCHAFFER: Delores Winters, a 10th grader. She just transferred here this year from Middlepoint High School.

MR. RANDOLPH: Well, what did you want me to do? Would you rather that I tell her the good news?

MISS SCHAFFER: I think it would be better if you did. Remember, though, the winner was to read his essay before the student body at the assembly this Friday.

MR. RANDOLPH: Oh, yes, I'd almost forgotten. *(Pause)* Well, have her come in and see me the first chance she gets. I wouldn't take her out of class though.

MISS SCHAFFER: No, I wouldn't, but she does have a study period this hour. Would you want me to send for her?

MR. RANDOLPH: Yes, please do.

(Miss Schaffer begins to leave, but stops when Mr. Randolph speaks)

MR. RANDOLPH: And Miss Schaffer, have one of the secretaries come in, would you please?

MISS SCHAFFER: Certainly.

Exit Miss Schaffer

(Delay of about ten seconds. Secretary enters, pausing in doorway)

Enter Secretary

MR. RANDOLPH: Come in, Miss Evans; I want you to take a letter.

SECRETARY: *(Sits in same chair Miss Schaffer used)*

MR. RANDOLPH: It's to Mr. and Mrs. Winters. You can check our files to get his first name. Their daughter is Delores Winters, so you can insert the proper first name.

"My dear Mr. and Mrs. Winters—On behalf of the faculty—and the Committee on Americanism Week, I take great pleasure in announcing—to you—that your daughter has been selected"—no, make that, "that we have selected the essay of your daughter—from the entire student body of Centerville High School—as the outstanding essay on Americanism." Let

Appendix Four

me see—"We wish to compliment you on behalf of the"—ahh—"fine work that your daughter has displayed. We trust that"—ahhh—"in the future, your daughter will continue to display her abilities and talents and that on many occasions you will have call to be—proud of her achievements. Yours sincerely, Wilber A. Randolph"—so and so. *(Rises from chair)* Would you read that back to me?

SECRETARY: "My dear Mr. and Mrs. Winters: On behalf of the faculty and the Committee on Americanism Week, I take great pleasure in announcing to you that we have selected the essay of your daughter from the entire student body of Centerville High School as the outstanding essay on Americanism. We wish to compliment you on behalf of the fine work that your daughter has displayed. We trust that in the future your daughter will continue to display her abilities and talents, and that on many occasions you will have call to be proud of her achievements. Yours sincerely, Wilber A. Randolph, Principal of Centerville High School."

MR. RANDOLPH: Very good. *(Paces)* Type that, and bring it in for me to sign, please.

SECRETARY: Yes, sir.

Exit Secretary
Enter Miss Schaffer

MISS SCHAFFER: *(Walks to Mr. Randolph)* Oh, Mr. Randolph, Delores Winters is here to see you. Shall I have her wait?

MR. RANDOLPH: No, send her in. *(Seats himself behind desk)*
Enter Delores Winters

MR. RANDOLPH: Come in, Delores. Here, sit down. *(Rises and helps her to a chair)* Now, then—have you any idea why I've sent for you?

DELORES: *(Delores is dressed very simply, and is a plain-looking girl. It is obvious that she feels uneasy, and she is not very attractive. Stands timidly before Mr. Randolph until he offers her a chair)* No, ... s . . ir.

MR. RANDOLPH: Well, I've got good news for you. What would you say if I told you that you won our Americanism essay contest? Isn't that a surprise?

DELORES: *(Straightens up, looks uneasy. She says nothing, but sits, thinking about what she has just heard. Then she registers joy, thinks again about what she heard, now registers* fear, *and finally begins to sob)*

MR. RANDOLPH: Now, now, there's no need to cry. You should be happy. Why I've just written a nice letter to your parents telling them how proud we are of you. *(Rises and walks over to Delores)*

DELORES: *(Crying more, and with her hand in front of her face, Delores still makes no attempt to speak)*

MR. RANDOLPH: *(Laughingly)* Why you've almost got me believing that you're sorry that you won the contest. That's not true is it?

DELORES: *(Slowly lifting her head, still sobbing, Delores shakes her head, yes)*

MR. RANDOLPH: *(Somewhat alarmed)* Yes? You mean you're not glad you won?

DELORES: No!!! *(Sniffling)*

MR. RANDOLPH: I'm not too sure I understand just what you mean. Why on earth would you be crying like this?

DELORES: Be . . . cause . . . I . . . stutt . . .er! *(Delores' stuttering is characterized by long pauses and blocks at the beginning of words. Also long pauses between words)*

MR. RANDOLPH: Oh, is that all? Well, we all stutter once in awhile. Why just the other day I stuttered over the word Mississippi! I said Mass-a-sippi or something like that. But that didn't bother me. Everyone does that once in awhile.

DELORES: . . . You . . . don't . . . un . . . der . . . st . . . and . . . I . . . .stutt . . er all the . . . t . . ime.

MR. RANDOLPH: *(Concerned)* I see! *(Meditates)* How long have you been stuttering? Like this, I mean.

DELORES: For . . . a . . . about . . . sev . . . en . . years.

MR. RANDOLPH: Hmmm. Well, didn't you ever try and do something about it?

DELORES: *(Sobbing still)* What . . . is . . the . . re to do?

MR. RANDOLPH: Well, isn't there some way to cure stuttering? I'm sure there must be.

Appendix Four

DELORES: Mother . . . and Dad try . . t . . o help me. They make m . e . . . s . . . low down. B . . ut it doesn't d . . o much goo . . . d.

MR. RANDOLPH: *(Mr. Randolph rises and walks around room while thinking out loud)* Well, there's got to be something done—but what? *(To Delores)* Look, Delores, I don't know too much about stuttering, but I intend to find out—and when I do, I'm sure that we'll settle your problems.

DELORES: B . . ut, will . . I . . h . .ave . . to r . . ead my paper be . .fore the assembly?

MR. RANDOLPH: So that's what's been worrying you. Of course not. We'll just announce that you won the contest, and that will be that!! Now you just forget all about it. I'll get in touch with you when I find anything out. So don't you worry, Delores.

Curtain

MODERATOR: No, don't you worry, Delores. But, unfortunately, that is something that is easier said than done. For Delores *is* worried and she had good cause to be. Imagine your having to go through life with a problem such as hers. No, it isn't very nice for a little girl to have such a handicap; in fact, it isn't very nice for any one to have that handicap. It's not an easy pill for a person to swallow. Now comes the problem: what to do to help Delores? It is easy to diagnose, but not so easy to remedy. Mr. Randolph is faced with a real problem now. How is he to solve it? Unfortunately, Mr. Randolph is not familiar with the field of speech and hearing therapy. Since it is such a new field, this is an understandable fact. Certainly Mr. Randolph is interested in his students, and for this reason intends to do something to help Delores. Centerville is a small town, and even if he knew of a clinician, the chances are that he would assume the Board of Education incapable of hiring one due to the expense. He does not know that the State may be able to give financial aid.

And so, Mr. Randolph does the only thing that he knows to do. If the school had a speech program, he could refer this case to the speech teacher. It is doubtful that even a speech teacher without the proper training in speech correction could handle a case such as Delores Winters'. So, he calls upon the only other person whom he feels is qualified for the job: the English teacher, Miss Johnson.

Helen Johnson was graduated from the State Teachers College in 19.... Since that time she has been teaching English at Centerville High School. As an English teacher, she is known to be an efficient, good-natured, and popular person. She is a favorite with all of her students, and a teacher who employs originality and consideration in her teaching. However, Miss Johnson is hardly the person to deal with the problem of Delores Winters. It is like asking a plumber to repair a leak in Boulder Dam. He has neither the facilities, nor the exact training needed for such a job, to say nothing about the experience. He may make an attempt, but one wrong step, the results could be disasterous. So it is in dealing with something as delicate as a person. Intentions may be good, but one wrong step, and you might cause irreparable damage.

And so we find Miss Johnson speaking to Mr. Randolph. After five meetings with Delores, she has realized that her problem is more than she is capable of handling.

Curtain

MISS JOHNSON: *(Seated by Mr. Randolph's desk)* Mr. Randolph, where do I go from here? I'm about at the end of the proverbial rope. When I said I would try to help Delores I knew then my attempts would be futile.

MR. RANDOLPH: *(Seated at desk)* I was afraid of that. Well, so far what have you done?

MISS JOHNSON: About the only thing I knew to do was to purchase a book on speech disorders. The book said that relaxation was essential, so, I'm having Delores relax.

MR. RANDOLPH: And what is that doing for her?

MISS JOHNSON: Frankly, not too much. Although she had told me quite a bit about herself, her environment, and friends.

MR. RANDOLPH: Such as?

Appendix Four

MISS JOHNSON: Such as why she even wrote an essay in the first place. It seems that it was an assignment for her civics course. It was being graded on the basis of a term project.
MR. RANDOLPH: I had wondered why she had written one. Well, where *do* we go from here. I'll admit, it's beyond me. I wonder how many other students have similar problems. We should be able to do something to help them.
MISS JOHNSON: I have a suggestion, Mr. Randolph.
MR. RANDOLPH: Let's hear it.
MISS JOHNSON: About a month ago I saw an article in a National Education Journal about work of this kind being done at the University clinic. Luckily, I saved the article. *(Hands paper to Mr. Randolph)* Here you can see for yourself. It's entitled, "The Wonder of Speech and Hearing."
MR. RANDOLPH: *(Reading aloud)* "An extensive program on the various disorders of speech and hearing is being conducted at the State University. The work taking place is in the form of group and individual therapy. Among the disorders that are treated at the clinic are cleft palate speech, cerebral palsy speech, articulatory disorders, delayed speech, cases involving aphasia, and restoration of speech for laryngectomized persons . . . . " By golly, Miss Johnson, I think you've hit on something. *(Looks over article)*
Curtain

MODERATOR: Yes, Miss Johnson did hit on something. The first thing that Mr. Randolph did was to write to the State Department of Education. They referred him to the placement bureau of the State University which located a certified speech and hearing clinician. Once located, the clinician made a call on Mr. Randolph. We now find Miss Baker, the speech and hearing clinician, discussing the need for speech correction.
Curtain
MR. RANDOLPH: *(Seated at desk)* I'm glad you were able to come to Centerville, Miss Baker.
MISS BAKER: I came just as soon as I received word from the University.

MR. RANDOLPH: I suppose you know why I asked to see a clinician?

MISS BAKER: No, all they said was that you wanted to speak to a clinician. That's all I know.

MR. RANDOLPH: Well, there's more to it than that. It's been brought to my attention that Centerville needs a speech correctionist. Do you mind if I ask you a question that will probably sound ridiculous?

MISS BAKER: By all means, please do.

MR. RANDOLPH: Well, this may sound strange coming from a school principal, but just what is a speech and hearing clinician qualified to do? In other words, what kind of problems can you deal with?

MISS BAKER: Well, Mr. Randolph, that question is not as ridiculous as it may sound. Many people have never heard of speech clinicians, and therefore, many people have no conception as to our work.

MR. RANDOLPH: I'd say you could put me in that category.

MISS BAKER: *(Smiling)* Well, to begin with, a certified, and I emphasize that word *certified*, clinician deals with such problems as poor articulation—that is, words that are mispronounced due to causes other than occasional missing of a sound, like "wabbit" for rabbit. And we work with voice cases, voices that are either too high or too low, or unpleasant sounding voices. Then we try to help the person who stutters, or has trouble in getting words to come out. People who have cerebral palsy, and cannot speak because of it, also come under our realm, plus those children or adults who have a cleft lip, or palate, or you may have heard it called by the name "harelip." And finally, in dealing with children, we work with the problems of delayed, or retarded speech. Of course, this is just a brief resume.

MR. RANDOLPH: *(Somewhat astounded)* Do you mean to say that you can cure all those things?

MISS BAKER: Now I didn't say cure! After all, we're not magicians. What we attempt to do is to help people overcome their problems. Sometimes the results will be permanent; other times the results are out of our hands. Children and adults with brain injuries such as cerebral palsy or aphasia represent complicated problems to the clinician. But what we do is help the person make the necessary adjustments in an attempt to live in society, unashamed and free from the thought of being what we might call different. It's impossible to say, "I can cure you of stuttering." A reputable clinician would never make such a statement.

MR. RANDOLPH: I see. I imagine it takes a lot of time and patience for this sort of work.

MISS BAKER: Yes, time and patience are the words for it. But cooperation shortens the time, and helps me have more patience. It's a cooperative process between myself, the child, and the parents.

MR. RANDOLPH: The parents? How do they figure in speech therapy?

MISS BAKER: It is up to the parents to re-enforce the work which we do. You see, we only work with the child an hour or so a day, while he is with his parents the majority of the time. That is also why the teacher must cooperate with the clinician. They, too, play important roles with the child. So you see, it takes mutual effort: the clinician to direct, the teacher to follow-up, and the parent to continue the work in the home.

MR. RANDOLPH: Then you have to deal directly with the parents.

MISS BAKER: Yes, that is a very important factor in the final success of the child.

MR. RANDOLPH: Well, Miss Baker, I think it's worth a try. If you're willing to take the job, consider yourself hired!

Curtain

MODERATOR: Centerville High School began a program in speech and hearing therapy. The State was only too glad to give the Board of Education the sum of $1,000 toward her salary. Once hired, Miss Baker investigated the speech of every child in the school. Those whom she felt needed work on speech were called to her office for talks. A surprising number of students sought her help. In the case of Delores Winters, the girl who stuttered, Miss Baker began therapy immediately.

Miss Baker was introduced to the teachers and staff of the school. She told them about the program in speech correction and how the teachers could cooperate with her.

Centerville High School has started an important program for its boys and girls to become better citizens. It is the job of our school to prepare the youth of America for its responsibility in later years. Good speaking habits are a vital aid to this goal. If your school does not already have such a program of speech and hearing therapy, consult the State Department of Education, or write to the nearest University Speech Clinic.

END

Now Hear This

Cast of Characters

MODERATOR, *off-stage voice (or visible)*
MOTHER, *middle-aged, or younger; understanding, but uninformed*
RONALD, *about twelve years old*
SECRETARY, *to Mr. Randolph*
MR. RANDOLPH, *principal of school*
MISS WEST, *Ronald's teacher*
MISS BAKER, *school speech and hearing clinician*

MODERATOR: Few of us ever stop to consider how fortunate we are in possessing the ability to hear. Hearing is something that is more or less taken for granted. When you awaken in the morning, you never stop to ask yourself, "Will I hear today?" As soon as you open your eyes, your ears begin to work. They may pick up a bird call, a streetcar, an automobile or a horn from an automobile, a noise from the room, or the sound from falling rain on the window sill. All of these sounds are heard unconsciously so that if I were to ask you what sounds you heard this morning, you would have to stop and think, and even then you would probably be unable to recall the sounds. We take our hearing abilities for granted.

However, try to imagine how you would feel if you awoke one morning and heard no sound. The absence of noise would be conspicuous. Let's stop right now and listen to the many noises that you can hear. *(Pause for 10 to 15 seconds.)* You probably heard the movement of chairs, or the rattling of a paper, or a cough, or heavy breathing, or a soft whisper, or even the watch ticking on your wrist; but you were, until this time, totally unaware of the sounds other than the ones coming from my voice. Imagine then, if you can, what your life would be like if you were never able to hear a sound or a noise. If you can visualize this emptiness of sound, you might be able to appreciate how a deafened person is reacting to his situation.

To the child or adult who has had hearing powers and lost them, there is the problem of having to adjust to a new environment—void of sound. This is a situation that is not very pleasant to consider; and yet, it becomes worse if we can say that such a situation could have been avoided.

Today, few schools realize the need for a hearing conservation program. However, in a recent study it was discovered that approximately 3 per cent of the school children have an educationally significant hearing loss, and at least another 5 per cent have losses that call for medical attention.

The first step in developing any good hearing conservation program is the hiring of a qualified speech and hearing clinician. In the play which follows, you will see how a hearing conservation program operates. Centerville Public Schools just recently hired a speech and hearing clinician and the program in hearing conservation and rehabilitation has been under way just a short time.

Scene 1

Curtain

SCENE: *A living room in the home of Mr. and Mrs. Foster. Table with magazines and sofa at left; table and two chairs on right.*

MODERATOR: The scene opens in the home of Mr. and Mrs. Foster. Mrs. Foster is doing some of her house work when her son Ronald enters. He has just come home from school, and is bringing home his report card. At a quick glance, you can see that Ronald is not too happy about the whole thing.

MOTHER: *(Mother is sitting center stage on chair darning*

Appendix Four

socks. A door slams. She looks up from her work) 'That you, Ronnie?

Enter Ronald

RONALD: Yeh! *(Ronald walks slowly over to Mother carrying a report card in his hand. He tosses card in her lap, picks up a magazine, and sits down with back to Mother)*

MOTHER: Hmmm, report card already? You don't seem too anxious this time! Holding out on me, I suppose. *(Ronald skims pages of magazine. Mother opens envelope and reads card. Face registers shock)* English, C??! Arithmetic, D??! What is this? *(She looks intently at card.)*

RONALD: *(No response)*

MOTHER: *(Indignantly)* Young man, what's the meaning of this *D* in Arithmetic—and that *C* in English? What happened to you this six weeks? *(Ronald still does not respond)* Ronald! I'm talking to you! Land sakes, talking to you lately is like—talking to this darning needle. *(Her voice is raised and she sits erect)*

RONALD: *(Ronald turns to his mother)* I knew you wouldn't like it!

MOTHER: Well, I should hope not. This isn't your usual work. Why this is the first time you've ever gotten a *D*—and a *C* in English—why last term you got an *A* in English—that's all you've ever gotten in English courses. Just wait 'till your father sees these marks!

RONALD: Well, it's not my fault. I can't stand Miss West!

MOTHER: Since when! You always liked Miss West. Why you even asked me to invite her here for dinner.

RONALD: Yes, I know; but—well, she's changed.

MOTHER: Oh, how could she change? *(Disgusted)*

RONALD: Ahhh, she has. She mumbles, and—well, I can't even stay awake in her classes.

MOTHER: Well, no wonder you got a *C*! Just you wait until your father hears about this. I'll bet he'll want to do something about this card.

RONALD: *(Shrugs shoulders and walks off stage. Mother sits back and continues to darn a sock)* What's for supper?

173

MOTHER: Lamb chops—but you deserve hamburger!
Curtain
MODERATOR: No, Mrs. Foster. I hardly think Ronald deserves hamburger. It could be that he deserves the proper attention which he obviously is not receiving. As time goes by, Ronald's grades are getting worse, and he is becoming a behavior problem. Slowly, Ronald's personality is beginning to change and what used to be a bright, alert, and intelligent boy is becoming a dull, inattentive, and uncooperative child. Every change has a reason behind it, and Mrs. Foster is concerned enough to attempt to discover Ronald's. At first she is set on blaming Miss West, Ronald's teacher; and so one day she decides to pay a visit to Mr. Randolph, the principal of Ronald's school.

We see, then, Mrs. Foster talking the matter over with Mr. Randolph.

Scene 2

Curtain
SCENE: *Mr. Randolph's office; desk, chairs, hat rack, etc.*
SECRETARY: Mrs. Foster here to see you, Mr. Randolph. Shall I have her wait?
MR. RANDOLPH: *(Mr. Randolph is seated at his desk)* No, send her in.
Enter Mrs. Foster
Exit Secretary
Won't you have a chair? *(Mr. Randolph rises and motions Mrs. Foster to sit down)* How are you, Mrs. Foster?
MRS. FOSTER: Fine, thank you.
MR. RANDOLPH: Now then, what can I do for you?
MRS. FOSTER: Well, I've come about my son, Ronald.
MR. RANDOLPH: I see. There's nothing wrong, is there?
MRS. FOSTER: I'm not sure. You see, as of late, there has been an obvious change come over him.

Appendix Four

MR. RANDOLPH: Change? What kind of change?
MRS. FOSTER: Well, for one thing, he isn't doing good in his school work like he use to. He's a good student, always gets A's or B's, and this time he brought home two D's! Last term he had one D. It isn't like him at all. That's why I'm worried.
MR. RANDOLPH: I see.
MRS. FOSTER: That isn't all. He never listens to me, and what's more, everytime I talk to him he just stares at me. Frankly, sometimes I think he's stone deaf!
MR. RANDOLPH: Who is his teacher? Perhaps she can give us some help.
MRS. FOSTER: Miss West is his teacher. And that's another thing. He used to like her, but now—he says she's mean, and —oh, Mr. Randolph, I'm worried about him.
MR. RANDOLPH: Have you spoken to Miss West?
MRS. FOSTER: No, I came to you first.
MR. RANDOLPH: Well, why not let me talk to Miss West about Ronald? I'll leave a note for her to see me after school. Then perhaps you can arrange for a time that you would be able to talk to her.
MRS. FOSTER: Thank you, Mr. Randolph. That will be fine. I hope I don't put you to any trouble. I realize how busy you must be. I know . . . .
MR. RANDOLPH: Now, I'm only too glad to be of help to you. After all, that's what I'm here for!
MRS. FOSTER: *(Stands)* Thank you again, Mr. Randolph.
MR. RANDOLPH: *(Stands)* You're perfectly welcome, Mrs. Foster. Do come back and see us again.
MRS. FOSTER: I will, Mr. Randolph. Good-bye.
Exit Mrs. Foster
MR. RANDOLPH: Good-bye. *(Mr. Randolph walks to door where Mrs. Foster exits)*
Curtain
MODERATOR: The initial contact has been made. But what can Miss West recommend? Let us look in on Mr. Randolph's office again. It is after school and Mr. Randolph is talking to Miss West.

Scene 3

Curtain
SCENE: *Mr. Randolph's office.*
Enter Miss West
MISS WEST: You wanted to see me?
MR. RANDOLPH: *(Seated at desk)* Yes, please sit down. It's about one of your students—Ronald Foster. His mother was in to see me this afternoon. It seems she's concerned about a *change* in Ronald.
MISS WEST: *(Sitting down)* Well, this may sound strange, but there *has* been a change in Ronald Foster. He was one of my best students until about two months ago. It's really hard to explain, but for some reason he has lost interest in school. In fact, he is becoming a disciplinary problem. He sleeps in class, and when I talk to him he just stares at me.
MR. RANDOLPH: Hmmm, that's about the same thing his mother told me. You don't suppose his hearing is bad, do you? We just bought Miss Baker, the speech and hearing clinician, a new audiometer for testing hearing. Maybe it wouldn't hurt to have his hearing checked.
MISS WEST: No, that's not a bad idea. I didn't know that the school purchased such a machine.
MR. RANDOLPH: Yes, we bought one last week. It serves to give screening tests as well as determining the amount of hearing loss a person has. Miss Baker was explaining it to me.
MISS WEST: Would you like me to speak to Miss Baker?
MR. RANDOLPH: Yes, maybe you two can discover something.
Curtain

MODERATOR: And so Miss West called Miss Baker, the school speech and hearing clinician. After talking the matter over, Miss Baker made an appointment to see Ronald Foster. Her first step was to give him an audiometric test to determine the presence of a hearing loss. As was expected, Ronald did have a hearing loss. Miss Baker then wrote a letter to Mrs. Foster informing her of the discovery. She advised the consultation of an otologist, a doctor who specializes in the diseases of the

Appendix Four

ear. Naturally, this information came as a shock to Mrs. Foster, who had never suspected a hearing difficulty in her son. And so, Mrs. Foster made an appointment with Miss Baker to discuss the matter further. We see, then, Mrs. Foster talking with Miss Baker.

Scene 4

Curtain

SCENE: *Miss Baker's office; desk, chairs, small tables and chairs for students; toys on the tables.*

MISS BAKER: *(Seated at desk)* You see, Mrs. Foster, when I discovered that up until very recently your son was not only a good student, but a model pupil, I began to suspect the reason for this sudden change to be something beyond his control.

MRS. FOSTER: *(Seated in chair near desk)* But what about his hearing? Is he going to be—deaf?

MISS BAKER: No, I don't think you have to worry about that. What did your doctor seem to think?

MRS. FOSTER: Well, he seemed to feel that his hearing loss was progressive, or one that may get worse; however, he also said he doubted if it would ever become serious if we take proper precautions now. He did say that a speech and hearing clinician could help Ronald. How will this affect his school work?

MISS BAKER: Well, for one thing, Miss West will put him near her so he won't have to strain himself. That was another reason I suspected a hearing loss.

MRS. FOSTER: What do you mean?

MISS BAKER: You recall he said Miss West mumbles? Well, if you've ever heard Miss West speak, you'd know she didn't mumble.

MRS. FOSTER: That also explains why he slept in class. He probably couldn't hear what was going on. Oh, I feel so bad to think of the way I treated him, and the things I said to him. What would you recommend that Mr. Foster and I do at home?

MISS BAKER: For one thing, you can speak slowly and dis-

177

tinctly without exaggerating your mouth movements too much. This will allow him a chance to read your lips and will also give him good practice. The thing you must not do is to let him think that he is different. Treat him in the same manner as you always have. Don't let this discovery make him pity or feel sorry for himself. After all, he is the same boy. So treat him that way.

MRS. FOSTER: I see.

MISS BAKER: Why don't you bring your husband in sometime. Then we can discuss the problem with him. I'm sure he'll want to help his son in any way that he can.

MRS. FOSTER: I will, Miss Baker. Well, *(Starts to rise)* I don't want to take up any more of your time. I realize how busy you probably are.

MISS BAKER: That's quite all right. I'm only too glad to help you.

MRS. FOSTER: *(Walks to door)* Thank you again for your help, and I'll speak to my husband and try to find a time to see you. Perhaps you could come over some evening?

MISS BAKER: Well, my evenings are rather full. But call me after you've spoken to Mr. Foster, and we'll see what arrangements can be made. *(Walks to door with Mrs. Foster)*
Curtain

MODERATOR: And so—Ronald Foster is at last being understood—the new hearing-conservation and rehabilitation program is in full operation for Ronald. Perhaps your school has a Ronald Foster, but his name might be Wilson or Stephens, or, well—you see what I mean.

Maybe, even your own son or daughter has a hearing loss which has been unnoticed so far. A speech and hearing clinician undertakes the responsibility of finding those children whose hearing is not good or who need to be referred for medical examination and treatment. For some children, lipreading, speech correction, or possibly a hearing aid will be advisable. The most important precaution, however, is to find the children with hearing losses early. Grade repetitions might be prevented, permanent damage to the hearing might be avoided, and many unnecessary emotional problems might be intercepted if hearing loss is discovered early enough.

We owe every student in our schools an opportunity to make the most of his individual abilities. We can help achieve this goal of our schools by giving children who are hard of hearing a chance to hear better—through auditory training, hearing aids, medical treatment, and lipreading.

If your school does not already have a hearing conservation program, consult your State Department of Education or the State Department of Health for information concerning procedures for securing services for your hard-of-hearing children.

END

Appendix Five: Suggested Programs for Parents and Teachers

A Program of Parent Education
A Series of 10 Two-Hour Meetings

Lesson I. Facing the Issue
1. Present Chapter I in lecture form.
2. Discuss materials presented.
3. Write a brief paragraph about your child's problem, stating in what way you had to face the issue. This may be shared in oral discussion.
4. Assignment: Write a short autobiography of your life since a handicapped child has been a part of it or read one of the stories listed at the end of Chapter I.
5. Film: *Your Children and You* (Chicago: British Information Services).

Lesson II. Hear Yourself as Others Hear You
1. Present Chapter II in lecture form.
    Demonstrate procedures.
2. Discuss and practice exercises.
3. Show film: *Your Voice* (Brooklyn College: Department of Speech), 1950.
4. Record "My Grandfather" on tape. This selection is in Appendix Two. Place all recordings on the same tape. Play back to the class. Let each person identify his own speech if he can. Each may write a short paragraph describing his speech.

Lesson III. Learning to Talk.
1. Present Chapter III in lecture form.
2. Discussion.
3. Parents may present brief review of child's speech development and any problems.
4. Continue work on parent's speech and voice started at the previous meeting. Practice in saying the

Appendix Five

vowels and consonants will call attention to how they are said. Choral reading of exercises found in Appendix Three will stimulate parents to follow the articulation of the leader.

Lesson IV. Speech Disorders: Types and Causes
   1. Begin period with brief speech drill on short phrases, using the choral reading approach.
   2. Present Chapter IV, "Speech Disorders." Discuss contents. Parents may want to relate chapter to own child.
   3. Films: *These Untrained Tongues* (Creative Graphics, University of Denver). *Introduction to Speech Problems* (Detroit: Wayne State University Audio-Visual Department).
   4. Assignment: Visit a speech clinic. Observe types of speech disorders.

Lesson V. Children With Delayed or Defective Articulation
   1. Present Chapters V and VI.
   2. Discuss in terms of individual children:
   Is the speech understood by you? By others?
   What about your child's speech is disturbing to you?
   How would you describe the child's speech?
   What do you think caused the trouble?
   3. Demonstrate testing of articulation with pictures.
   4. Film: *Speech Training for the Handicapped Child* (Chicago: National Society for Crippled Children and Adults, Inc., 2023 West Ogden Avenue). *Good Speech for Gary* (New York: McGraw-Hill, Text-Film Department, 330 W. 42nd Street).
   5. Make a picture articulation test (find words for this purpose in Appendix Two).

Lesson VI. Children With Stuttering Symptoms
   (Start period with a brief speech drill on consonants and short phrases.)

1. Present Chapter VII.
2. Discuss.
3. Show films: *Stuttering, From the Horse's Mouth* (State University of Iowa Film Library), 33 minutes. *Search: Stuttering* (State University of Iowa Film Library), 27 minutes.
4. Questions for discussion:
Can stuttering be cured?
Will a child outgrow stuttering?
Do stuttering children have any mental deficiency?
Do all children who repeat sounds become stutterers?
5. Assignment: Read a case history of a stuttering child or adult, or
Observe someone who stutters.

Lesson VII. Children With Cerebral Palsied or Cleft Palate Speech
1. Practice reading aloud in unison some of the materials in Appendix Three. The leader will say the phrase first with the class responding to her stimulation. An attempt is made for "clear-cut" articulation.
2. Make some reference to "Face the Issue," Chapter I, since parents with organically handicapped children have real problems of acceptance of the handicapping condition.
3. Present Chapters VIII and IX, followed by discussion.
4. Films: *Search: Cerebral Palsy* (National Association of American Business Clubs in cooperation with National Society for Crippled Children and Adults, 2023 West Ogden Avenue, Chicago 12, Illinois), 26 minutes. *Cleft Palate Speech in the Child* (University of Michigan Film Library), 30 minutes.
Discussion of films.

Appendix Five

Lesson VIII. Hearing Problems
1. Discuss Chapter X, "Is He Hard of Hearing?"
2. Select films from those listed at the end of Chapter X.
3. Questions for discussion:
   What are symptoms of hearing loss?
   What causes hearing problems?
   What should the parent do to help the child?
   What is a hearing conservation program?
4. Have parents act out the skit, "Now Hear This" (Appendix Four).

Lesson IX. Personality and Emotional Problems as Related To Speech
1. Present information based on Chapters XII, XIII, XIV, and XV.
2. Discussion:
   Based on questions at end of each chapter.
   Illustrations may be given by parents.
3. Films: See suggestions at end of Chapters XIII, XIV, and XV.

Lesson X. Reading and Speech
1. Present Chapter XI with particular attention to relationship between reading and speech.
2. Demonstrate how parents can help child at home by reading aloud to him.
3. Show how current reading materials may be adapted as speech lessons at home (Dolch cards, example).
4. Differentiate between phonics and phonetics.
5. The last hour of this two-hour period should be spent in summarizing the work of the course and "next steps."

Notes

This outline has been presented simply as a guide to the leader. The experienced clinician will be able to supplement and incorporate many additional ideas and procedures. If this program is presented at the university clinic, many resources will be available for illustration. For instance, the senior clinicians may present examples of therapy to the group of parents. Professors in speech pathology, audiology, and psychology may present lectures on pertinent topics.

A Program for Classroom Teachers

A similar outline may be followed for classroom teachers as suggested for the parents. However, some attention needs to be given to what the teacher can do in the classroom to help the handicapped child. Lesson I might be "Finding the Speech and Hearing Problems in the Classroom," instead of "Facing the Issue" as given in the parent's outline. In this lesson, demonstrations or recordings of the various types of speech problems will help the teachers to identify problems. An introduction to the use of the speech inventory included in Appendix Two should be given. The teachers may be assigned to use this outline in locating children with speech problems.

A session on "Speech Improvement in the Classroom" might be appropriate and helpful to the classroom teacher. However, Lesson V, "Children With Delayed or Defective Articulation," in the parent's outline is quite appropriate for classroom teachers. At this time, some demonstration of techniques in speech improvement may be given. The film, "Good Speech for Gary," shows the speech improvement activities in a classroom. The exercises used at the beginning of the meetings for the improvement of the parent's own speech and voice are also very important for the classroom teacher. The use of choral reading, ear-training drills, and phonetic activities are all helpful in the classroom.

The teacher's program may be supplemented by readings from references or mimeographed material handed out by the leader.

Appendix Six: Case History Sketches of Children With Speech Problems

Linda—a stutterer

Linda is a young, thirteen-year-old Negro girl who stutters. During speech, she covers her mouth and avoids looking at her listener. She blocks on the first letters of words.

She is a middle child with an older sister and a younger brother. The father, a doctor, is also a stutterer. The grandfather tried to change the father's handedness from left to right. The mother had no stuttering symptoms; she appeared calm and spoke with a pleasant voice. She appeared willing to help Linda.

The mother stated that Linda began to stutter at three years of age. She encouraged the child to "slow down and take your time." At age three-and-one-half, the pediatrician recommended a speech clinic which Linda attended for one year until she was almost five.

While Linda was ages seven, eight, and nine, she lived with her family in Germany. For the first time, she attended an integrated school. The mother stated that Linda came home with stories that the children didn't like her and wouldn't hold her hand when the games were played. She felt different from the other children for the first time in her life. Her stuttering became worse.

Linda has always been an excellent student in school. Her stuttering is worse during the school year. The prognosis for this girl is good since she is eager to improve her speech. She is intelligent and has some insight into her problem.

Questions

1. What do you think caused the stuttering?
2. Is it abnormal for children, age three, to hesitate in speaking?

Gary—husky and weak voice

Gary, five years old, had a husky and weak voice. His speech was almost unintelligible. His articulation was characterized by many substitutions and omissions. An examination of Gary's vocal cords revealed nodules. He was advised by the doctor to have a complete rest of his voice for one month.

Gary received speech therapy for five weeks. The goals were to work on two sounds s, and p, and to improve general intelligibility of speech.

If Gary responded to vocal rest, he was to resume speech therapy with some attention given to voice improvement. The case history did not indicate factors producing the organic condition of the vocal folds.

Questions
1. What might cause nodules to appear on a child's vocal folds?
2. How can parents encourage a child to give his voice a rest?
3. Have you noticed any children with poor voices? Describe.
4. Indicate how a parent can help children to use voices properly.

Michele—nasal voice

Michele, ten years old, had a nasal voice which would make one think she had a cleft palate. All of her vowels were sounded through her nose as well as many of the consonant sounds.

She had her tonsils out and the nasality appeared more extreme than ever. Both the mother and father have sinus trouble. Michele also has some trouble with allergies.

The soft palate seemed long enough to keep air from going through her nose; however, the palate was inactive. Helping Michele to use her soft palate more effectively and giving her training in differentiating between nasal and non-nasal sounds would lead to improved voice quality.

Micky—articulation

Micky, a sturdy seven-year-old boy, had speech characterized by many omissions, substitutions, and distortions of consonants. His behavior in the clinic was withdrawn. He appeared tense about his speech and worked very hard. He was also quite awkward in general movements.

His sister, six years old, also had unintelligible speech. Many of the substitutions, omissions, and distortions were similar to those made by Micky.

When Micky was about two years old, he was fretful because his mother was very ill and unable to care for him. At this time, the mother tried to anticipate some of his wants so he would not cry. He soon reverted to sign language although he had started to use words.

Between the ages of two-and-one-half and three, Micky had severe cases of measles, chicken pox, and mumps.

Psychological tests indicated that Micky was operating within the normal range of intelligence. He was right handed. Perhaps his delay in speech may be traced to his serious diseases and the anticipation of his wants during the speech readiness period.

With speech therapy, Micky improved his speech. Children soon quit teasing him for his poor speech. While Micky received therapy, his sister also obtained help for her speech. The mother attended a parent education class so she could learn what to do to help the two children at home.

Irene—hearing loss

Irene is an attractive, alert little five-year-old girl with a hearing loss. She lost her hearing rather suddenly. Although her speech was never very clear, it deteriorated markedly according to her mother after the onset of the hearing loss.

Irene communicates with gestures. She is an excellent lipreader. She vocalizes but the sounds are only syllables.

According to Irene's mother, she babbled very little and was slow to talk. She was never clear in her speech. The parents are eager to help Irene since she will be old enough to enter school next fall.

As a result of the diagnostic examinations at the clinic, it was recommended that Irene be enrolled in a school or class for the deaf or hard of hearing. Some consideration should also be given to the wearing of a hearing aid.

Questions
1. Why should a child with a serious hearing handicap be enrolled in a special class for the hard of hearing?
2. What was an early symptom that the child was having hearing problems?

Charles—cleft palate

Charles is a tall, lanky boy of fifteen years with a cleft-palate voice and faulty articulation. He is in the eighth grade, about two years behind his normal age group. Charles was born with a cleft lip and a cleft palate.

His medical history reveals that he had three operations: cleft lip surgery at the age of two-and-one-half years, cleft palate surgery at the age of three-and-one-half years, and another cleft palate surgery at the age of ten. His teeth need orthodontic attention.

Charles has had speech therapy for several years in the public schools and at the college clinic. Therapy has included attention to the unvoiced sounds *th*, *k*, *s*; improvement of orality of sounds; and improvement of confidence.

Speech therapy often takes many years for the person with cleft-palate conditions, even though successful surgery has been performed. Charles had learned many of the skills but needed to continue practice to make his speech automatic.

Jack—cerebral palsy

Jack is a twelve-year-old boy with cerebral palsy. His articulation is almost unintelligible. Much air is directed through the nose rather than through the mouth. As he speaks, his jaw drops frequently and he is unable to raise his tongue to the roof of his mouth with easy coordination.

Emotional stability has been a factor for improvement. The mother is a hard, dominant, driving person with the model of perfection for the child physically and in speech. She criticizes

Jack unjustly in his presence. The clinician is not sure the mother is justified in her criticisms, since she has always found the boy to be dependable and cooperative. Unfavorable comparisons have also been made between Jack and his sister. His father has been a good companion to the boy, but now he is ill in the hospital from a disease which will keep him from working again. The boy is not allowed to visit him since he may cry.

Speech therapy has consisted of relaxation, blowing activities to direct breath and sounds through the mouth instead of the nose, and working on specific sounds.

Questions
1. What are some of the problems in this child's life?
2. What does the mother need to do to help?

Appendix Seven: National Agencies

Alexander Graham Bell Association for the Deaf, Inc., The Volta Bureau, 1537 35th Street, N.W., Washington 7, D.C.
Publication: *Volta Review*.
American Hearing Society, 919 18th Street, N.W., Washington 6, D.C.
Publication: *Hearing News*.
American Speech and Hearing Association, 1001 Connecticut Avenue, N. W., Washington 6, D.C.
Publications: *Journal of Speech and Hearing Disorders; Journal of Speech and Hearing Research; Asha;* and *Directory* of members specified as to clinical certification.
Department of Health, Education, and Welfare, Washington 25, D.C.
Division of Special Education, Consultant on Speech and Hearing
Office of Vocational Rehabilitation
National Education Association, 1201 16th Street, N.W., Washington 6, D.C.
Association of Childhood Education
Council for Exceptional Children
Publication: *Exceptional Children*.

Index

"A Day at the Farm," 156
Adjustment, to changing society, 146
Ames, L.B., 138
Anderson, V., 21, 27, 100
Articulation:
  causes, 53
  classification of sounds, 18
  mechanisms, 17
  norms for production of sounds, 49
  production of difficult sounds, 18–49
  sounds in order of difficulty, 51
Artley, A.S., 108
Attitudes, definition, 145
Auer, J., 150

Backus, O.L., 48, 84, 151
Bacon, F., 157
Baker, L., 9
Baruch, D.W., 10, 115, 138, 147, 151
Beasley, J.E., 27, 48
Behavior problems, causes of, 130–132
Belgum, D., 67
Berry, M.F., 27
Betts, E., 109
Brown, A.C., 150
Buck, P.S., 9
Butler, K.G., 151

Carlson, E.R., 74

Carrell, J.A., 101
Cerebral palsy:
  ataxic, 70
  athetoid, 69
  causes, 70
  five levels of speech problems, 72
  incidence, 68–69
  resources, 73–74
  spastic, 70
  speech therapy, 70–72
  team approach, 70–71
  types, 69–70
Chapin, A.B., 150
Children's Emotions (a film), 138
Children with speech problems, case histories of, 185–189
Clancy, J.N., 84
Class for Tommy (a film), 127
Cleft lip, types, 77
Cleft palate:
  and community resources, 83
  and parent's role, 83
  causes, 78–79
  incidence, 76–78
  prognosis for speech improvement, 80–81
  sex distribution, 76–77
  speech training, 80–82
  steps in therapy, 82–83
  team approach, 79
  types, 76–77
Cleft Palate Speech in the Child (a film), 84
Coleridge, S.T., 157

Davis, H., 100

Delayed speech:
  auditory stimulation, 45
  causes, 42
  early treatment, 44—45
  moto-kinesthetic treatment, 44—46
  stimulus-response method, 44—45
  visual method, 44—45
Dolch, E.W., 109
Dolman, J., 21

Ear, diagram of, 91
Ears and Hearing (a film), 101
Ears That Hear (a film), 101
Eckert, R.G., 150
Educational adjustment:
  and parent's role, 117—118, 122
  and teacher's role, 122—124
Eisenson, J., 21, 27
Emotional adjustment, and speech problems, 129—130
Emotional problems:
  fear, 136
  jealousy, 133—135
  negativism, 133
  temper tantrums, 135
  treatment of, 132—133
English, O.S., 138
Eubank, H.L., 150
Exercises:
  for prolongation of vowels, 157
  for short phrase, 157

Faegre, M.L., 150
Fairbanks, G., 21

Fessenden, A., 21
Fiedler, M.F., 100, 150
Films, 10, 21, 40, 58, 67, 75, 84, 101, 109, 127, 138, 147
Finch, S.M., 138
Fitch, J.W., 101

Gardner, W.H., 84
Geis, S.B., 150
Good Speech for Gary (a film), 58
Gratke, J.M., 74
Greenberg, K.R., 159

Hearing, and speech, 88—
Hearing conservation:
  educational follow-up, 92—93, 98
  medical follow-up, 91, 97
Hearing impairment:
  and parent's role, 94—96
  and personality, 92
  and speech therapy, 92—93
  and teacher's role, 95
  high frequency loss, 87—88
  incidence, 89
  symptoms, 90
Hearing Inventory, 152
Hearing rehabilitation, procedures, 90
Hedgecock, L.D., 101
Heiner, M.H., 9, 100
Henry, L.D., 84
Hoversten, G., 100
Huber, M., 74
Hymes, J.L., 115, 138, 150

Index

Ilg, F., 138
Intelligence:
  and speech, 118—120
  definition, 117—118
  levels of, 121
  mentally retarded child, 122—123
  normal child, 121—122
  Stanford-Binet Test, 120
  superior child, 123—124
  testing of, 120—121
Introduction to Speech Problems (a film), 40
Irwin, R.B., 27, 48, 58, 126, 150, 156
It's a Small World (a film), 138

Jackson, J., 102
Johnson, W., 9, 27, 40, 58, 100, 150, 151
Jones, M.V., 58

Karnes, M.B., 126
Karr, H.M., 21
Keaster, J., 100
Kellogg, R., 138
Kemper, J., 84
Kirk, S.A., 126
Kirk, W.D., 126

Language development, language comprehension period, 23
Larynx, main functions, 33
Leader, P., 9
Levinson, H.J., 75
Lillywhite, H., 150
Listening Eyes (a film), 101

Loewy, H., 126
Longerich, M.C., 75
Longfellow, H.W., 158

Matthews, J., 48
Mayer, J., 138
McDonald, E.T., 84
McKibben, S., 75
Medical consultants, 4—5
Menninger, C.W., 147
Menninger, W.C., 147
Mental hygiene:
  basic needs, 4, 6
  facing reality, 5—8
  parents face problems, too, 7—8
Monroe, M., 109
"My Grandfather," 156
Myklebust, H.R., 101

National agencies, 190
"Now Hear This," 171—179

Ogilvie, M., 151
Out of the Shadows (a film), 75

Palate, parts of, 78
Parent education, a suggested program, 180—183
Parent's report, 154
Perlstein, M.A., 75

Personality:
  and intellectual facts, 114
  and speech, 110
  meaning of, 111–112
  physical characteristics of, 112
Phair, G.M., 84
Phelps, W.M., 75
Phillips, J.W., 101
Picture articulation test, words for, 154–156
Pitch:
  determining optimum, 14–15
  flexibility, 15
Place in the Sun, A (a film), 75
Poetry Time (a recording), 58
Poole, I., 50
Poole's Index, sound development, 50
Pronovost, W., 151
Pronunciation, 16

Rasmussen, C., 151
Reading problems:
  a penalty, 103
  and brain dominance, 105
  and parent, 106–108
  and speech, 102–103
  and teacher, 106–108
  causes, 104
  diagnosis, 104
  incidence, 102
  treatment, 106–108
Reading readiness, 103
Recordings, 58
Rehabilitation of Patients With Clefts of Lip and Palate (a film), 84
Rheingold, H.L., 150
Ronnei, E.C., 101

Russell, D.H., 109
Rutherford, B.R., 75

Say and Sing (a recording), 58
Schuell, H., 150
Scott, L.B., 58
Search: Cerebral Palsy (a film), 75
Search: Hearing (a film), 101
Search: Stuttering (a film), 67
Shakespeare, W., 157–158
Shere, M., 75
Shyness (a film), 147
Social adjustment:
  and speech, 141–142
  effect of cultural influence on, 144–145
Sorrenson, F.S., 21
Sounds Around Us (a recording), 58
Speech, and physical growth, 24
Speech development:
  babbling period, 23
  encouragement to talk, 24–25, 46–47
  first vocal response, 22
  parent's responsibility, 24–26
  sound-imitation period, 23
  stages, 22–24
Speech disorders:
  causes of, 33
  definition, 35
  degrees of adequacy, 31
  diagnosis, 35
  incidence, 36–38
  penalties of, 32
  rehabilitation, 38–39
  types, 36–38
Speech Inventory, 153
Speech mechanism, 33
Speech readiness period, 45

Index

Speech stimulation, 25—26, 51, 54—56
Speech therapy, sound deviations, 53—57
Speech Training for the Handicapped Child (a film), 58
Strang, R., 126
Strazzulla, M., 48, 127
Streng, A., 101
Stuttering:
 and mental attitudes, 62
 and physical health, 61
 and treatment by parent, 63—65
 and treatment by teacher, 63—66
 causes, 60—61
 conditions associated with, 59—60
 description, 59—60
 environmental factors, 63
 incidence, 37
 treatment, 61—66
Stuttering, From the Horse's Mouth (a film), 67
Symonds, P.M., 151

Teacher education, a suggested program, 180—184
Templin, M.C., 50
Tennyson, A., 158
"That Others May Talk," 159—170
That the Deaf May Speak (a film), 101
These Untrained Tongues (a film), 40
Thompson, J.J., 58
Thursday's Children (a film), 101
Tongue-tie, 33—34
Travis, L.E., 10, 115, 138, 151

Tucker, C.D., 10
Turner, T.A., 75

Utterback, W.E., 151

Van Riper, C., 27, 40, 48, 58, 67, 151, 156
Voice:
 breath support, 13—14
 enthusiasm, 19—20
 intensity, 15—16
 quality, 13—14
 rate of reading, 16
 relaxation, 13

Warkomski, R.C., 58
Wedberg, C.F., 10
Wells, C.G., 84
Westlake, H., 75
Why Can't Jimmy Read (a film), 109
Wisconsin Cleft Palate Story, The (a film), 84
Wood, K.S., 151

Yedinack, J.G., 102
Your Children and You (a film), 10
Your Voice (a film), 21

Zedler, E.Y., 48

DISCHARGED
DISCHARGED
DISCHARGED
DISCHARGED
DISCHARGED
DISCHARGED
DISCHARGED
APR ... 1970
AUG ... 1970 DISCHARGED 1970
DISCHARGED
OCT 8 1970 DISCHARGED OCT 16 '71 DISCHARGED 1975
DISCHARGED 1983
DISCHARGED OCT 28 DISCHARGED 1984
DISCHARGED JAN ... '71
NOV ... 1971
DISCHARGED NOV 30 '72
DISCHARGED 1973 NOV 28 1974
DISCHARGED
APR 20 DISCHARGED 1970
MAR 14 '71 DISCHARGED
DISCHARGED
DISCHARGED
DISCHARGED 1975
AUG 2 1985